To

Judith

The Layman's Guide to
PSYCHIATRY

About The Author

James A. Brussel, M. D., is Assistant Commissioner of Mental Hygiene of the State of New York. A graduate of the University of Pennsylvania School of Medicine, Dr. Brussel took advanced studies at Columbia University and the New York State Psychiatric Institute. He holds the American Board Certification in psychiatry and neurology. A Lt. Col. in the Army Medical Corps Reserve, Dr. Brussel served in World War II as Chief of the Neuropsychiatric Service at Fort Dix. During the Korean conflict, he was Chief of the Army's Neuropsychiatric Center at William Beaumont Army General Hospital in El Paso, Texas. He has lectured at William Smith and Hobart colleges and at Yeshiva University, and is a consultant to the New York Police Department and the city courts.

Dr. Brussel has edited the psychiatry section and related units of *Collier's Encyclopedia* and *Annual* since 1948. He is the author of *The Rorschach Psychodiagnostic Method,* and has made many contributions to professional journals.

The Layman's Guide to

PSYCHIATRY

JAMES A. BRUSSEL, M. D.

Preface by Paul H. Hoch, M. D., Commissioner
Department of Mental Hygiene, New York State

BARNES & NOBLE, INC.   NEW YORK
Publishers   •   *Booksellers*   •   *Since 1873*

This is an original Everyday Handbook (number 220). It was written by a distinguished author, carefully edited, and manufactured in the United States of America in accordance with the highest standards of publishing.

Foreword

A primary objective in writing this book has been to present the highlights of modern psychiatric knowledge for the general reader who may be concerned with an emotional or mental problem, or who may wish to know more about mental illness and the role of psychiatry. Another objective, equally pressing, has been to do this in straightforward, easily understood language. The author is aware that it would be impossible, even if it were desirable, to do away completely with technical terms, since to oversimplify the language would, at the same time, oversimplify the concepts—concepts which are often elusive in their nature and content. For this reason, semantic control is most needful in the area of psychiatric thinking. Whenever feasible, however, the author has translated technical terms into everyday language; in other instances, the reader may wish to refer to the Glossary.

The book has two general divisions. The first, comprising Chapters 1 through 12, lays the foundation for an understanding of psychiatric principles and describes the categories of mental and emotional illness. Chapters 13 through 17 take under consideration the practical aspects of adjustment to life at several levels, and conclude with a discussion of religion and love.

No one "slant" or approach to mental disorder is given preference in these pages. The time has long since passed when the basic principles of Freud were held in serious doubt. Accordingly, such hypotheses as the concept of the unconscious, the psychosexual levels of personality adjustment, and others deduced from psychoanalytic investigation, underlie the explanations and discussions of the neuroses and the psychoses. But with regard to interpretations and applications of these principles by the various schools, the different approaches have been fully discussed; organic methods of treatment and the holistic concept have been given full consideration.

The reader must understand that this book is not to be used as an instrument for "do-it-yourself" diagnosis and treatment. It is an exposition and a guide. The author's hope is that (1) readers in general will recognize that the broad problem of abnormal behavior is something to be handled medically rather than legalistically; (2) that the book may help readers who are emotionally disturbed but possess insight into their condition; and (3) that relatives and friends of mental patients, particularly of those who are institutionalized, will have a clearer picture of what has been and what is being done to overcome the obstacles unique to this medical specialty.

The Layman's Guide to Psychiatry should also be an aid to medical students, general practitioners, psychologists, social workers, occupational therapists, and volunteer hospital aides. All those who have frequent contacts with individuals and families in stressful situations where mental disorder plays a role—legislators, welfare officials, educators, attorneys, and clergymen—should find this book useful and informative.

I am profoundly indebted to George La Fond Cantzlaar for his invaluable editorial guidance and assistance, and to my wife Audrey, for her devoted encouragement and tireless efforts in behalf of this book.

J. A. B.

Dr. Brussel presents us with a very readable compact textbook of psychiatry for the layman. The book is, of course, principally of value to an educated layman who is able to understand and follow some of the psychiatric principles around which this book is constructed. Dr. Brussel's approach could be called an eclectic one, drawing ideas from different psychiatric schools and sources and blending them into a comprehensive whole. This book well reflects our contemporary thinking in psychiatry. It must be emphasized that psychiatry is in flux and no one knows to what extent our present concepts will turn out to be correct because there is still a great deal that is unknown in this field. Sometimes this unknown is covered by glib generalizations and rationalized explanations. This is especially common in psychiatric books which are written for laymen. Dr. Brussel has tried to avoid this difficulty by properly being more technical in some of his concepts than is usual in books for laymen, but I believe this is for the better because sometimes the lay public has the impression there is no technical body of knowledge, but simply a conglomeration of opinions expressed by different people. I believe that any person who is interested in a field needing scientific technique and understanding has to acquaint himself with the particular background of this science and Dr. Brussel's effort to fulfill this need is effective.

Paul H. Hoch, M.D.

Table of Contents

The Layman's Guide to

PSYCHIATRY

1: Behind the Human Mind

It is a simple matter to describe the common experiences that pass constantly through our minds—the thoughts, desires, hates, and loves familiar to our consciousness. But to uncover the roots of these experiences, to explore what lies behind the human mind, is a most difficult undertaking. The individual tends to assume that he is in full control over his thoughts and actions. It comes as a shock when he discovers that his thinking and behavior can often be traced back to very early experiences of which he is now totally unaware. He finds it hard to realize that within his own mind are submerged forces—mental forces—which can drive him against his better judgment (or even against his will) to act in an unreasoning or unreasonable manner. These submerged forces whose immense hidden power was first explored by Sigmund Freud, make up a vast reservoir of memories stored in the depths of the mind, always ready to emerge at the conscious level.

Nothing experienced is completely forgotten. Thus, a bitter mental shock in infancy may appear to have sunk into oblivion, but it can be awakened in later life during a time of stress. The mental shock has been merely *repressed,* held out of consciousness until a new emotional conflict recalls to memory the earlier experience and brings it again to the level of consciousness. Such repressed experiences and their accompanying emotions are the complexes, of which one of the most familiar is the Oedipus complex which derives its name from Sophocles' dramatization of a son's extreme attachment to his mother. The case histories of countless disturbed or neurotic men demonstrate the results of this complex, for these men have been so intensely affected by their repressed emotion that they are unable to establish suitable relationships with women. They may remain unmarried or, if

1

they do marry, they may set up unattainable standards for their wives, expecting them to be second mothers.

Let us consider the "normal" child. Throughout infancy his entire world is the narrow confines of his crib. All that he encounters are the four walls of his little universe, with a heaven above from which appears at regular (sometimes too frequent) intervals a goddess. This goddess is something akin to magic, with her soft tones, her solicitous kindness, and her warm protective breasts with their unrationed supply of nourishment. Extremely significant is the infant's awareness that food is part of the mother. It does not take the child long to learn that his mother is a combination of security, happiness, and sustenance. These early experiences and the accompanying emotion of sheer joy become deeply imbedded in the infant's unconscious and form a core of mental life which, in spite of the thick layer of mature experiences that will follow, is never forgotten. Deep within him, be he banker, bookkeeper, professional athlete, machinist, or what you will, the grown man unconsciously remembers that, in his entire career, at no other time was he so completely secure, blissfully happy, and well-fed as when he was a baby in his mother's arms. No matter how sophisticated or practical-minded he may become, he will never really "forget" this episode.

EARLY EXPERIENCE

Two types of very early experience have been shown to exert a profound influence in shaping the mind and personality of each human being. These are the experiences of infant feeding and toilet training. In the first two years of life, these experiences are so predominant that they are associated with two distinct phases of development: the oral stage and the anal stage.

The Oral Stage. Feeding is, unquestionably, the prime feature of daily life from the very first day of existence. The infant soon realizes that he will be rewarded by smiles and kisses when he empties his bottle. As new items of food are added to his diet, he learns that his security is more solidly cemented when he pleases mother by eating the egg or cereal, or by drinking the orange juice. Her pleasure is gained in proportion to his co-operation in catering to his own welfare *via mouth and stomach*. Consequently, there develops from this gastrointestinal association with the mother a symbolic attachment to the entire digestive process which has come to signify a measure of security.

If the *sucking period* is handled judiciously by the mother, the infant will go forward normally in his psychosexual development; that is, there will be no adverse personality traits in later life which can be traced to earlier mismanagement. A baby is quite a tyrant; almost from the time of birth he learns that his mouth is a prime weapon in commanding the world as he knows it. Because howling and crying bring him prompt gratification of his drives and desires, he has a sound reason for holding the oral cavity in highest esteem. Such a baby, if all his whims are satisfied by an overanxious mother, goes on in life, continuing to pamper his mouth, eating well, depending on oral satisfaction to allay frustration. He may turn up in later life as the chain smoker, the fingernail biter, the chewing gum addict, etc. He is often seen in later life as the glib talker, the high-pressure salesman, teacher, actor, or executive.

Now let us reverse the procedure. What of the baby whose mother religiously ignores his screams, adamant in her determination not to "spoil" him? His unconscious mind believes that mother does not love him, that bellowing for her attention is a futile gesture. And so, there may be generated in him the feeling that he is unwanted, unattractive, and scorned. As he matures, he must rely on his own resources and retreat further into his shell. In adulthood he is the introverted individual, the misanthrope, often the researcher or writer, the artist, the "man in the background." When such an individual turns his back on the world completely, he becomes the recluse, perhaps the schizophrenic.

The *biting period,* initiated by the eruption of teeth, immediately follows the sucking period. The infant now finds an outlet for his aggression in which he can add to vocal expression of anger or resentment. He can inflict pain; he can *bite.* If, however, this does not subjugate the world about him (particularly, the mother), if, in fact, it brings him punishment—pain for pain—he quickly learns that life holds many bitter, frustrating situations; he finds that one must "toe the mark." This, of course, is a lesson which we must all learn and, by and large, we profit from it. But should the experience too seriously impair the infant's confidence in his own strength he may become timid, completely lacking in aggressiveness. His interpersonal relationships will be tenuous; he will have difficulty making friends. Such a person will be deprived of the healthy and warm advantage of being able to confide in others—parents, relatives, friends, or associates.

On the other hand, the biting baby whose sadistic attack is completely unchecked, even feared, learns not to waste his strength. He conserves it for the strategic moment when he will want to conquer resistance to his whims totally and unconditionally. As an adult, he is the individual with the caustic, sarcastic, denunciatory phrase. He gains leadership by cowing those about him and ruthlessly smashing those in his way.

The Anal Stage. Generally, when the infant is able to sit erect without assistance (at about the sixth month), he is launched on his career of acquiring toilet habits and self-restraint. This new direction of the mother's interest places greater emphasis on the gastrointestinal system. From birth, the baby, having learned that he is able to "create" something, has been happy with his bowel and bladder productions, and has been "permitted" to pursue this pleasurable activity without any indication that his mother does not share his attitude. Suddenly he discovers that such conduct displeases her. Now he learns for the first time to associate pain, displeasure, and distastefulness with the intestines and the rectum.

This dramatic brake on his previously uncontrolled bowel behavior will remain a prime incident in his unconscious. Later on, the first threat to security may set off a sequence of events well known to physicians: tremor, crying, sweating, rapid pulse, palpitation, a quivering sensation in the pit of the abdomen, and even wetting and soiling. The experience is not, however, entirely traumatic; it also has beneficial effects. The infant now realizes that there are times when the demands of reality (i.e., society) require him to think of others besides himself. He learns responsibility and self-reliance.

The baby's emotional response depends not so much on *what* the mother does but *how* she does it. If she rewards him with smiles when she places him on the toilet, encouraging him to use this new method, the experience will be relatively free of unpleasant associations. Severity and relentless discipline may, however, leave their marks on the infant's unconscious, and may be manifested later in life as undesirable personality traits. The grim, uncompromising mother, while she may accomplish her immediate goal, also runs the risk of creating an embittered individual—one who will feel that he inhabits an unappreciative universe, peopled by enemies out to "take everything." He becomes the misanthrope, the hoarder, the withdrawn person. The mother with a passion for clocklike regularity, who places the baby on the toilet at precisely the same time, day after day, may well be molding a future precisionist who, as an adult, will be intolerant of error, a stickler for promptness, and painfully tidy and orderly. On the other hand, the mother who only changes the baby when "she gets around to it" could be rearing an individual who will be slovenly, careless, irresponsible, unreliable, lazy, and procrastinating. Obviously a middle road must be found that combines both affection and firmness.

THE UNCONSCIOUS

To Sigmund Freud we are indebted for the concepts which explain the persistence and power of early experiences. Freud's fundamental concept of the unconscious has undergone many adjustments in interpretation and application, but it remains essentially as he expressed it, and it is basic to the understanding of what lies behind the mind, or psyche. According to Freud, this mental mechanism which accounts for all of the thoughts, feelings, and behavior of human beings consists of three components: the id, the ego, and the superego.

The id is an inner storehouse of psychosexual energy, which Freud calls the "libido." It is the central core of the personality, the motive power that constitutes our basic instincts, drives, and desires. Like a maturing tree trunk, it gradually develops a hardened exterior as a result of its exposure to the numerous restrictions which the outer world imposes upon the conscious life. This hardened exterior is the ego, the mental self, the "bark" of the personality. As time passes, the ego becomes aware of which drives and desires the id will be allowed to release in its endless search for gratification. The ego learns this through the action of a third mental component, the superego or conscience, which begins to develop with the birth of the individual. The superego evolves initially from the intimate relationship between child and mother. It is not implied here that the superego is morally superior in any sense to the ego and the id; it is merely the guide-and-check mechanism that recognizes the restrictions and dictates of the outside world. The superego enables us to make distinctions between "right" and "wrong" according to the standards of the social and religious environment in which we live.

DEFENSE MECHANISMS

The "outer bark" or ego is the integrating force of the personality, the catalytic agent that gives each of us individuality. Through the ego we learn to distinguish between self and not-self; each new experience develops in us those characteristics which make us unique, and we grow to hold this ego very dear. Any assault upon the integrity of the ego creates discomfort, if not intense feelings of guilt. To soften such blows, we have recourse to a number of devices called "mental mechanisms" or "dynamisms," constituting the large range of behavior performed by an individual's mental equipment. Such behavior or functioning may be defensive, aggressive, or compensatory, either dominantly one of these or involving combinations of the three. In addition to the mechanism of repression, previously described (see page 1), several other mechanisms are recognized in psychiatry. The moving force behind these mechanisms, as well as behind their thought content, is emotion (*e*, out + *moveo*, move) or "affect," which may attach itself to or invest almost any thought content. This investiture of an object or idea with feeling is technically known as *cathexis*.

When a person is infected, the body reacts in a protective manner to combat the onslaughts of the invading germ. At once there is a battle between the organism and the individual. Similarly, in the face of mental injury or under stress, defensive or compensatory mechanisms are brought into play. A common example of this is the phenomenon of mutism in psychotic stupors, a categorical form of defense against the communication to others of any or all ideas of the patient. The symbolic reproduction of repressed ideation or thinking is another example of a defense mechanism at work.

Types of Defense Mechanisms. The following are the principal methods of defense employed by an individual in adjusting to reality. Most persons have used some or all of these mechanisms in adapting to various life situations.

IDENTIFICATION. According to Freud, identification "is the original form of emotional tie with an object." The infant at first is completely identified in his emotional life with his mother and also with the entire environment. His first months are largely occupied in differentiating himself from the environment, in separating from himself all those that are "not I," i.e., separating subject from object. The "I" normally becomes more and more clearly differentiated as the infant matures (but in disorders such as schizophrenia, the individual experiences regression to the early period of vague personal identity and the sense of close relationship with the environment). Persisting as an unconscious mental mechanism, identification in the normal individual is merely the self-appropriation of qualities belonging to another individual or object, or the transference of these qualities from one person to another. How often do we "identify" ourselves with the hero of a book we are reading? Notice how children assume the mannerisms of relatives and teachers. When any characteristic or belief gained by identification remains with us permanently, we add it to what Freud termed our "ego ideal," i.e., the idealized person we would think ourselves to be.

INTROJECTION. Introjection is the mental absorption of environmental qualities by an individual. An example is the fastidious housewife who feels uneasy at the slightest disarrangement of her home, such as a picture hanging crookedly on the wall. Through the mechanism of introjection the individual appears to draw the outer world within the circle of his interests and so reacts disproportionately or inappropriately to the details of his environment. Introjection may also serve to turn toward oneself emotions such as anger or hostility which were originally directed toward another.

PROJECTION. Projection is the process of attributing to another the ideas or impulses that belong to oneself. It gives what appears to be objective reality to that which is actually subjective. The individual's use of a projective mechanism implies that what he attributes to another he regards as undesirable; consequently he may blame someone for his own mistakes. Once the individual has externalized the undesirable trait, he firmly believes that it originally emanated from without. Thus, a certain type of paranoid patient, beset with unconscious homosexual impulses, projects these urges upon some man or men in the environment and then struggles against the urges as though they arose from outside sources. Projection is an unconscious process and is purely defensive in nature.

Introjection and projection are exactly opposite. Such pairing off is characteristic of many emotional or affective expressions; they tend to occur in two sets of symptoms that are diametrically opposed. Like a pendulum, the affect seems to swing in one direction and then in the opposite. Affective symptoms, therefore, tend to occur in pairs, such as projection and introjection, love and hate, masochism and sadism, etc. This capacity for opposite types of expression is known as *ambivalency*.

DISPLACEMENT. Displacement involves the attachment of inappropriate emotions to various objects or ideas. The student who blames his teacher for his own inability to learn and the tennis player who blames his racket for his own court deficiencies are examples in which affect (emotion) has been displaced from a proper to an improper place, usually environmental. This mechanism, seen in both normal and mentally disordered individuals, is an escape by which one's mind avoids, or defends itself against, personal shortcomings.

SUBSTITUTION. Displacement occurs when the emotion upon which attention is focused is shifted from object to object. The mechanism of substitution begins to function and moves the point of view to objects to which the emotion is attached, as they are successively substituted for one another. Displacement and substitution are, therefore, merely two aspects of the same dynamism, and the objects or objectives which become successively invested with emotion, because the quality of the affect is the same, may symbolize each other.

SUBLIMATION. By means of the mental mechanism of sublimation, repressed sexual impulses are deprived of their specific erotic content and aim and are deflected toward new goals, nonsexual in nature and socially acceptable. Many unacceptable sexual desires may be sublimated as creative effort in music, art, and literature. The man with a strong unconscious homosexual urge that is thwarted by a rigid superego can sublimate the perverted drive—effect a compromise between the unconscious and reality—by giving himself constantly to males in a nonsexual manner (as in the case of the schoolmaster, Mr. Chips). Among the many activities that may be expressions of sublimation are: social welfare work, nursing, teaching, etc.

TRANSFERENCE. In the psychotherapeutic setting, progress is impossible unless the patient has implicit faith in the psychiatrist. This implies a free-flowing emotional exchange, known as transference. In this uninhibited manner the patient can transfer emotions to the therapist, who may stand for a parent, or a lover, or an enemy, depending on the episode in the patient's life under discussion at the time.

CONVERSION. Conversion is the process by which a painful emotional conflict is converted into socially acceptable, physical symptoms by means of which the individual is able to maintain his rapport with reality and yet satisfy the unconscious demand for release of emotional tension caused by inner conflict. Thus, the mother who is remorseful for slapping her child may later develop complete numbness of the hand. Conversion hysteria—a Freudian term denoting a condition partially akin to the modern concept of psychosomatic illness—implies unconscious feelings of guilt and the need for punishment. This is a purely masochistic mechanism, in which realistic, consciously painful, outer gratification relieves the unconscious, but equally painful, emotional struggle.

RATIONALIZATION. Rationalization is the mechanism by which an acceptable explanation (not the true reason) is advanced for conduct; it effectually disguises and covers up the genuine reason from the subject himself, as well as from others. Human beings frequently believe that they perform certain acts for reasons other than those which really motivate them. Man's innate tendency, undoubtedly an expression of his narcissism, is to think and do as he wishes, and then discover an acceptable reason for so doing and thinking. Rationalization may be a deliberate or an unconscious procedure in any given individual. The physician constantly keeps this in mind in his contact with patients, since probably no one is free from the distortions produced by this mechanism; indeed, the doctor often must be careful that he is not guilty of distortions resulting from his own rationalization.

Unconscious Nature of the Mechanisms. The reader must not assume that in defense mechanisms we are including the "alibis" that people invent at the conscious level. Sublimation, repression, and the other dynamisms operate beneath the surface of awareness. The individual himself is firmly convinced that "he never wanted that job anyhow because the responsibility was too great" or that he is "glad he came in second in the race because all that publicity for the winner would bother him." The man who has experienced difficulty in forming effective interpersonal relationships and who becomes absorbed in stamp collecting believes that he has taken this step because it is much more satisfying than to move freely and easily among his fellows. And so it is with projection, identification, and the other defensive mental reactions.

It should be borne in mind that the previously defined mechanisms are not examples of "abnormal" thinking or acting. The employment of one or another of these is perfectly normal. Indeed, it can often lead to truly constructive gains for the individual; much of the great work of the world has been undertaken and accomplished by people who found a need to compensate for some frustration through the process of sublimation.

MASOCHISM AND SADISM

Just as there are positive and negative electrodes, so in the human psyche there are two opposite forces. These contrary, but complementary drives, both erotic in nature, are masochism and sadism. In our masochistic moments we are tender, self-sacrificing, unwilling to inflict pain or hardship; under the influence of the sadistic component of our psyche we are dominant, tyrannical, eager to inflict pain. The two components are somewhat oversimplified in the dichotomous terms love and hate. Actually, a very fine balance between the two indicates emotional maturity; paradoxical as it may strike some readers, the completely masochistic, "loving" person is not normal, and would be well-nigh unbearable as a spouse or an associate. Extremes of either type abound in history: Joan of Arc, who met death as a reward for love of country (the masochist), and Caesar, who pursued a relentless campaign to master the world (the sadist). In the field of mental disorders, one can recognize the sadist in the paranoid individual who is supremely conceited and smug, free with vicious insult and sneering remark; the masochist is often seen in the woman who, in the menopause, is depressed, agitated, and self-condemnatory.

INDIVIDUALITY

We have seen that the principal components of the mind (the id, ego, superego, defense mechanisms, and instinctive drives) are common to all human beings. In fact, the members of any species have many traits in common, traits which either persist throughout the life of the individual or may be manifested only at given periods, and which make up the pattern that is referred to as "the norm." Diversions from this pattern or a portion of it are regarded as "abnormalities." While this concept provides a neat definition, when it is applied too literally it can lead to unsupportable generalities. For even among the common characteristics there are differences. "Like peas in a pod" at first sounds entirely logical, but not if the peas are examined closely. When one turns to human characteristics, be they physical, intellectual, or emotional, what is most striking is not the similarity of people, but the infinite variety of individual differences.

Consider the field of medicine. Through arduous effort and painstaking study, symptomatic pictures have been delineated for a host of clinical entities. But whereas nine hundred and ninety-nine cases of pneumonia will be readily recognized by the typical rise in temperature, cough, expectoration, and chest pain, the one thousandth case *may show none of these signs.* Furthermore, the degree of temperature will vary widely among the individuals, as will the violence of the cough and the intensity of the chest pain. Although this by no means invalidates medical knowledge of pneumonia, it must give us pause should we place too much reliance on "types." As the main highway of medicine narrows to the side roads of the specialties, the exceptions to the rule become more frequent, and nowhere is this more applicable than in the realm of psychiatry. The further one probes into the human mind, the more one is convinced that no two psychic mechanisms are the same; therefore, no two personalities are identical.

Personality and Character. Because these words infringe upon each other, and both appear in the language of psychiatry, it is desirable to delimit their meanings. Personality can be defined as the sum total of behavioral characteristics by which one is recognized as an individual. From the psychiatric point of view, although the end meaning is the same, a dynamic mechanism is implied. Aside from referring to the outward picture that the individual presents as a compromise with his environment, personality is also thought of as the complex of inner forces that enables a human being to adjust his instinctual drives to the demands of the external environment. Indeed, it may help us to understand the psychiatric interpretation of personality if we bear in mind the use of the *persona* in Greek drama. The *persona* was a mask worn by an actor to identify the mood or character of the role he was portraying; remnants of this are seen in the familiar masks for comedy and tragedy. Since the individual must come to terms with the world about him, he creates an image (or mask) of himself. This image, known as the *ego,* is his personality as others see it.

Character, on the other hand, has the more special meaning of the composite of individual traits as they relate to the mores of the group. "Character disorders," a diagnostic entity in psychiatry, includes behavioral and attitudinal phenomena which are in conflict with society's standards. Strictly speaking, this is the only accepted use of the word character in psychiatric terminology.

Environmental Groupings of Personality. At the risk of oversimplification, it is suggested that personality types can be observed on an environmental basis. Proceeding from the more general to the specific, these personality types may be ethnic (racial), national, provincial, communitarian, or familial in origin. The extent to which any of these categories rests upon a biological foundation is not known, but the fact is inescapable that in one or another of them it is possible to identify personality types with relative ease. The "typical" Scandinavian, raised in a rugged terrain where agriculture is difficult and in a climate that is generally harsh, appears to be concerned principally with a search for security, nourishment, and warmth. He is usually stolid, unexcitable, and coldly practical. Even his music reflects the rigors of his life. On the other hand, the individual reared in the Mediterranean region or the tropics, accustomed to lush vegetation, is usually unhurried (as seen in the *mañana* spirit and the *siesta*), given to romanticism with spurts of excitability, and often unmindful of practicalities. His music and his guitar-strumming proclivity reflect the influence of his environment on the molding of his personality.

Within a national group one finds sectional types. The Catalonian, the Basque, and the Andaluz are all Spaniards, but their emotional make-up as well as their physical characteristics are noticeably different. This is true, too, of the New Englander, the Midwesterner, the Texan, and the man from the Cotton Belt. One can pursue this line of thought almost indefinitely, down to communities and even to neighborhoods. In general, however, the more selective the group, the greater is the influence of environmental factors, as can be seen in sections comprising "the other side of the tracks," Park Avenue, and Catfish Row, all of which, in one form or another, are found in communities across the country.

Even within the family group, wide variations are found. It is not uncommon to discover a well-adjusted family with six children one of whom suddenly develops a mental disorder. Why should this occur? Under the same discipline, the same ethnic standards, the same economic and social pattern, should not *all* the children have well-adjusted personalities? The answer to this problem is still beyond us. Thus, we tend either to fall back upon the "constitutional" explanation and, with a sigh of resignation, mutter, "He was born that way!" or to seek "excuses" for asocial behavior in surface factors, such as inferior living conditions, poor economic status, and the like.

2: *Ills of the Mind*

As researchers uncover more and more causes of mental and emotional disturbances, it becomes increasingly difficult to define mental "disorder" or "disease." There are no neatly labeled packages of psychiatric conditions; even the diagnostic categories now generally accepted cannot be said to be "the last word." Any such affliction, ranging from a mild, fleeting sensation of uneasiness, through a depression, to a frank psychosis with all the "trimmings"—hallucinations, delusions, and aberrant behavior—is a variable clinical affair.

Centuries ago, someone who behaved strangely or talked incoherently was thought to be "possessed of evil spirits." Today it is accepted that disordered thought and action are overt expressions of mental illness. The need for prompt diagnosis and treatment is recognized and psychiatry has emerged from its early position as the esoteric branch of medicine. We should not, however, be deceived; there yet remains a hesitancy to go "all out" in this evolution. We still hear that "psychiatrists think everybody is crazy," although it would be equally logical to say that "physicians think everybody is sick."

The most stable individual may suddenly show signs of emotional upset or personality disorder in response to unusual and stressful circumstances, and this response may be either mild or severe. The college student about to face an examination may "freeze" unexpectedly in a state of panic. In a similar fashion, the patient en route to the operating room for a mere tonsillectomy, becomes apprehensive, frightened, and tremulous because of an unconscious fear of death. In the present clinical sense, these are manifestations of mental, emotional, or nervous disorders; but the manifestations alone are not necessarily evidence of mental illness. It is the degree of their intensity, their persistence, and the total picture of the individual's adjustment to his life problems that tell the story.

As an analogy, let us consider the respiratory system which is subject to many gradations of disorders. One may have the "sniffles," a severe cold, an attack of influenza, or suffer the ravages of pneumonia or tuberculosis. Degrees of severity are observed in disturbances of any organ system. Is it unreasonable to assume that this principle also applies to illnesses of the mind? But observe how differently people react to so-called physical affliction on the one hand and mental on the other. The sufferer from a respiratory disorder, the cardiac patient, the person who has undergone heroic surgery for a recalcitrant gallbladder—these people do not lose prestige among their fellows. Indeed, the first, with his accounts of the rise and fall of fever, the second, with vivid complaints of palpitations, and the third, with dramatic recitations of preoperative and postoperative events, are often regarded as "life of the party" types. What is the counterpart of this situation in the other, the "forbidden," field? Let it be known that the somewhat anxious or depressed person has consulted a psychiatrist and his arrival at any gathering is marked by raised eyebrows, a momentary lull in the conversation, curiosity, and the tacit query, "Does it run in his family?" No, we have not completely emerged from the chrysalis of primitive thinking that has retarded the advancement of psychiatry for centuries. Even with contemporary enlightenment, there are many who regard mental disorder as a single isolated clinical entity, totally unrelated to all the other afflictions of mankind.

One of the major obstacles to a better understanding of mental disorders is the lack of agreement on a single standard for "abnormal" and "normal." The "bizarre," the "peculiar," the "ludicrous," the "sensational"—these present no problem. It is in the much more common fields of human behavior that agreement is found wanting. Even psychologists struggle with this problem. Test after test has been created, but accurate estimation of personality has yet to be realistically achieved. A person may be described as "charming" or "unappealing," or as "having a chip on his shoulder," but no personality can be indicated in terms of percentages, pounds, or plus and minus signs. Unlike an exact blood test, no personality examination can be precise because there is no such thing as a "normal" personality to serve as a

standard of comparison; personality must be measured qualitatively rather than quantitatively. Furthermore, there is the possibility that the subject of a test may "unconsciously" lie in his
responses to the examination questions, thereby giving a distorted
or unreal picture of his personality.

In some degree, so-called normalcy depends on contemporary
social dictates, mores of the community, and racial and national
cultures. The Irish-American girl who puffed a clay pipe as her
great-grandmother might have done, would be an oddity in modern society, but her own filter-tipped cigarettes would have
shocked her ancestors. If the usually phlegmatic Anglo-Saxon
suddenly started speaking explosively, using forceful gesticula-
tions characteristic of the Latin, he would probably be regarded
as behaving abnormally. Cultural identification is an important
factor in one person's judgment of another's normalcy. Even in
the physical fields, the concept of normality is only an arbitrary
one, founded almost wholly on statistics. What, indeed, is a
"normal" height? Certainly it cannot be the mathematical average, for if this is true, great hordes of people are "abnormally"
tall or short. Normalcy, then, must include a broad area on both
sides of the average. The reader is therefore invited to apply
this concept to problems of human behavior and thinking. As
this becomes more and more acceptable to him, he will be better
able to understand that mental illness, like the physical disorders
previously mentioned, can be just a bit away from comparatively
good health, then farther away and more incapacitating, and,
finally, completely destructive to the individual's way of life.

While it has not been possible to set up a graduated scale that
delineates such increasingly serious levels of mental illness, an
attempt has been made to separate illnesses of the mind into
larger categories as recognized by the American Psychiatric Association. These, with parenthetical indications as to where each
is discussed in this book, are as follows:

1. *Transient situational personality disorders* (Chapter 4,
"Everyday Tensions and Anxieties").

2. *Psychophysical autonomic and visceral disorders* (Chapter 5,
"Psychosomatic Illness").

3. *Psychoneurotic disorders* (Chapter 6, "The Deeper Tensions
and Anxieties—Psychoneurosis").

4. *Psychotic disorders* (Chapter 7, "Flight into Another World —Psychosis").

5. *Personality disorders* (Chapter 9, "Sociopathologic [Asocial] Behavior" and Chapter 10, "Addiction").

6. *Mental deficiency* (Chapter 11, "Mental Retardation").

7. *Chronic brain disorders* (Chapter 12, "Epilepsy," Chapter 13, "The Formative Years," Chapter 14, "The Years of Change," and Chapter 15, "The Later Years").

8. *Acute brain disorders*. These include neurological conditions such as meningitis, encephalitis, brain tumor, brain injury, et al. It is quite possible for a *chronic* brain disorder to be complicated by an *acute* brain disorder. For example, the patient who has been suffering with chronic hardening of the brain's arteries may suddenly be stricken with a severe cerebral hemorrhage with signs and symptoms of a paralytic stroke. For practical purposes, the reader should recognize that acute brain disorders, with and without psychic manifestations, are usually so precipitant and obviously indicative of immediate medical assistance, that he would automatically seek help for someone who is stricken. Certainly, the last thing the reader would do in such a circumstance, would be thumb through a book to find out whether the patient is "really ill." The drama of the attack is self-evident and calls for prompt action.

3: Roots of Mental Illness

"Doctor, why am I so nervous?" "Why can't I sleep?" "What makes mother so depressed and agitated?" "Is it my fault that I have a mentally retarded child?" These and many similar questions are constantly being put to physicians by persons concerned over their own emotional and mental problems or those of their relatives and friends. Theirs is a healthy curiosity, for it is essential to an effective mental hygiene program (the "public health" aspect of psychiatry) that the causes of mental illness be understood. Thus, early unfavorable signs may be noted and preventive measures taken or treatment administered promptly.

The psychiatrist, every bit as much as the layman, would welcome with open arms a quick, easy, uncomplicated answer to the question, "What causes mental illness?" Unfortunately, two kinds of roots spread beneath the surface in a mental disturbance: they are *underlying causes and precipitating factors*. The distinction between them is seen in the following example. Confronted by complaints about her son's petulant mood and disruptive behavior, a mother may declare, "Small wonder my boy is a nervous wreck! Not only is he burdened with a rigorous school program and hours of home study assignments, but we are pressed for money and he has to work nights to earn a few dollars." But is the explanation that simple? Clinical examination of the son, supported by detailed history-taking, reveals a lad who has always been shy, diffident, asocial, seldom if ever smiling or laughing, with few friends, and given to burying himself in books. Psychological testing points to incipient schizophrenia. It is not, then, the hard work that has made a "nervous wreck" of him; actually, a budding psychosis has begun to be reflected in his behavior and attitudes. Hard work, which has shown that he "can't take it," was only the last straw, the *precipitating factor*

18

in a long line of shocks, challenges, and irritants which in another individual might serve to develop patterns of reaction leading to good psychological and social adjustment. The cause of this youngster's maladaption must lie deeper—within his personality structure or within the biological (physicochemical) complex that provides the machinery for his reaction to the world about him.

Both underlying causes and precipitating factors can be either exogenous or endogenous. Examples of exogenous factors (arising from outside the individual), are everyday threats and frustrations, economic stress, cultural clashes, and social restrictions. Examples of endogenous factors (arising from within the individual) are metabolic disturbances, infectious diseases, and circulatory changes. While endogenous factors are receiving increasing attention in research efforts, the strong interplay of the exogenous and the endogenous is not to be ignored.

CHEMISTRY AND MENTAL ILLNESS

In research laboratories, normal human beings have been made temporarily but profoundly mentally ill by the administration of a substance (as yet unnamed) prepared from the blood of schizophrenic patients. There is a strong suggestion from this that schizophrenia, which fills half the beds in mental institutions, is a hereditary or constitutional, rather than a psychological, disease. Such experimental findings also seem to point the way to the development of chemicals that will block the secretion of this peculiar substance and thereby effect a return to mental stability. The stage may thus be set for the creation of a sort of "Wassermann" test for schizophrenia in which the blood of persons suspected of being schizophrenic would be examined to determine whether the offending substance is present. It has been theorized that this substance may be a protein, one of the large molecules containing 40,000 or more atoms which facilitate all the chemical functions of living organisms. Apparently, this protein is not found in normal human beings.

In their pursuit of these findings, biochemists have been working on the premise that some substance or substances within the organisms breaks down the communications of the central nervous system. It is known that the "signals" of this nervous system, in the course of being transmitted at neural junctions (synapses) are facilitated by acetylcholine and inhibited by adrenalin (epinephrine). Compounds that produce hallucinatory states (hallucinogens) are chemically related to adrenalin. They include sympathomimetic amines such as amphetamine, herbs used by primitive tribes (such as bufotenin and mescaline), and the most powerful synaptic inhibitor, serotonin. It has been demonstrated that LSD (lysergic acid diethylamide) produces a "psychosis-in-miniature" by increasing the production of serotonin in the body. Many of these inhibiting compounds share a similar nucleus (indole), one form of which (5-hydroxytryptamine) is found in normal body constituents such as serotonin and enteramine.

From the foregoing, it becomes theoretically conceivable that a breakdown in the metabolism of adrenalin or one of its related constituents could bring about excess production of the substances which inhibit transmission of impulses in the nerves, and that a different kind of metabolic disruption might produce excessive acetylcholine, leading to overproduction of impulses to the brain.

Ataractics (tranquilizing agents) were born out of this research. The synaptic inhibitory effects of a hallucinogen (e.g., mescaline) can be overcome by tranquilizers such as reserpine and chlorpromazine. It is also possible for these substances to block the action of serotonin and adrenalin on the nerves.

PHYSIOLOGY, THE EMOTIONS, AND THE MIND

The ductless glands (suprarenals, pituitary, thyroid, gonads, pancreas, parathyroids, and pineal), through the action of their secretions (hormones), are involved with the emotions and the psyche (mind). This is, in fact, the physiologic link that strengthens the concept of psychosomatic (mind-body) illness. Popular expressions, such as "I feel nervous" and "It must be his nerves," are not altogether unscientific when one considers the interplay of the nervous system and the other systems and organs of the body. From the psychological point of view, the autonomic nervous system enables us to "stay alive." It permits the body to pursue its everyday, "involuntary" existence, to react to impulses received from the sensory organs, and to innervate organs for "basic" living (heart, lungs, digestive tract, organs of elimination, etc.); this is the "animal living automatically" without the necessity of thinking. In contrast, the sympathetic. nervous system implies exactly what is meant by the word "sympathy"—feeling and thinking. It innervates ductless glands and voluntary muscles, and is involved in emotional control.

Oddly enough, in contemporary research the physiologic approach is returning to the views advanced many years ago by neurologists who described clinical conditions, the causative factors of which were associated with malfunction of the nervous system. These views are seen today in the increased importance of the holistic concept in medical practice (see Chapter 5, "Psychosomatic Illness").

Vagotonia. The tenth cranial nerve is a component of the parasympathetic nervous system. This nerve (the *vagus* or *pneumogastric*) is very extensive, sending branches throughout the body: within the skull, to the eyes, lungs, heart, and gastrointestinal and renal systems (to mention only the major areas). When the vagus predominates over the sympathetic nervous system or is stimulated (by a drug such as pilocarpine), signs and symptoms are produced which may be identified as vagotonia. These include constricted pupils and a cool, dry skin which, due to a sluggish cardio-respiratory activity, may become cyanotic (blue). With bodily processes generally slowed, pulse rate and blood pressure are pathologically diminished. The decreased respiratory rate implies faulty oxygenation of the lungs, particularly in the remote portions (the apices), and this renders the vagotonic individual prone to pulmonic diseases, notably tuberculosis. Excessive vagus influence in the stomach and intestines results in alternating diarrhea and constipation and in other gastrointestinal afflictions. Psychologically, such a person lacks nervous "drive," is indifferent, dull, retiring, and asocial. He is the tall, lanky individual, whose perpendicular growth is disproportionately greater than his lateral development. This is known as the *asthenic habitus* (or body type), the physical prototype of the schizophrenic.

Sympathetonia. Now let us turn to the sympathetic nervous system, which is so intimately involved with the ductless glands and emotions. Stimulation of this system by shock, drugs, etc., causes an outpouring of impulses to voluntary muscles and ductless glands. Among these, the suprarenals ("on top of the kidney") are of prime interest, because adrenalin (their hormone) causes dilatation of the pupils, perspiration, flushing, increased heart and lung action, tremulousness, and loss of control of sphincters (ring-like arrangements of muscles that control the intestines, bladder, and rectum). Thus fright, excitement, anger—indeed, any and all human emotional responses to unusual life situations —can bring about sympathetonia. The term for this body type is *pyknic.* Such a person's girth is disproportionately greater than his length. He is the rotund or pleasingly plump person recognized through his ruddy complexion, picturesque speech, dramatic gestures, impulsiveness, and tendency to swift decisions. He plunges into life wholeheartedly, *sympathetically,* "hotly." In everyday life the pyknic is apt to be the choleric supervisor, the wildly screaming spectator at the ball game, the raconteur, the "life of the party," the organizer, the high-pressure salesman, the "eager beaver," the exhibitionist. Sympathetonia is commonly associated with high blood pressure, "stroke," heart disease, and coronary thrombosis.

The Total Picture of the Nervous System. At this point the reader will begin to appreciate what is meant by the "holistic" approach: the study of man, not as several parts, but as a part of a world to which he tries to adjust, with its climate, geography, cultures, racial differences, etc. In adapting to this environment, he uses his body (with its organ systems), mind, emotions, and glands, and a certain heritage that has come down through countless ages (phylogenetically) with instincts and drives—all interwoven to make living possible. In this book the reader will find many references to drugs, emotions, environmental influences, illnesses, et al., which directly affect man so that he reacts in one direction or another through and with his nervous system.

It is obvious that stimulation of the sympathetic nervous system results in effects that can be produced by depression of the parasympathetic nervous system. For example, dilatation of the pupils results from homatropine drops (a belladonna derivative) in the eyes; cocaine has the same effect. The two nerve system components are better understood when we realize that the sympathetic (vegetative) nervous system, phylogenetically the older of the two, is primarily concerned with instinctive and affective (emotional) life, while the parasympathetic system is involved with nutrition and race preservation and is the means by which we "move" in life and are able to cope with environment.

Various Physicochemical Causes of Mental Illness. Malfunctioning glands can result in medical conditions which combine physical, emotional, and psychic features. For example, the inadequate thyroid produces such clinical signs as dry, scaly skin; sparse, lusterless hair; brittle nails; and low blood pressure. The affected individual tends to be dull, uncommunicative, listless, and indifferent to environmental stimuli.

Chemical and physical disturbances can also bring about simultaneous effects in pellagra, the "starvation disease," which is characterized by intestinal symptoms, skin disorders, and delirium, and may terminate fatally. Addison's disease, in which the suprarenals fail to function sufficiently, is characterized by anemia, weakness, fatigue, low blood pressure, slow pulse, and bronzing of the skin. With the suprarenals unable to respond to sympathetic stimulation, a vagotonia-like condition results (see p. 21).

Other physicochemical causes of mental disease are: hardening of the arteries, old age, syphilis of the central nervous system, various neurological conditions (brain tumor, St. Vitus' dance or Sydenham's chorea, and encephalitis lethargica or so-called "sleeping sickness"). Poisons such as lead, alcohol, and arsenic create clinical states accompanied by psychiatric manifestations. Organic causes also include head injury, heart and kidney diseases, menopausal changes, endocrine abnormalities, vitamin deficiencies, and exhaustive states.

The Comprehensive Viewpoint. The clinical inseparability of the chemical, physical, emotional, and psychic aspects of an individual is therefore obvious. The acceptance of this premise, along with an understanding of the associations among the nervous system, glands, muscles, and emotions, prepares us to comprehend what is implied by psychosomatic illness (discussed in Chapter 5), which the American Psychiatric Association categorizes as "psychophysiologic autonomic visceral reactions."

SYMPTOMATICS VERSUS DYNAMICS

Like the alchemists' search for the "philosopher's stone" which would turn base metals to gold, the pursuit of a panacea for the "cure" of mental illness arouses strong hope in the minds of men. A word of warning must therefore be issued to the reader to place the earlier discussion of chemical backgrounds in its proper perspective: such research is still in its infancy. Nor is this the whole story. Let us assume that science *does* discover that the lack of x substance in the body causes a psychosis, or that mental disorder arises from the presence of y, a poison. This chemicophysical "find" cannot explain why a particular individual will manifest his disorder as a manic-depressive. Nor can it explain why one schizophrenic is a paranoid, another catatonic, and another hebephrenic. Why? *Because no two psyches are the same.* The constituents of a red blood cell are standard in humans, the mechanism of oxygenation is a uniform physiologic process, but what is actually "normal," "subnormal," or "abnormal" in any one psyche is an ephemeral guess. Blood cells and respiratory functions can be neatly categorized; at the current stage of evolution in psychiatry, diagnostic classifications are more useful statistically than clinically.

The promising note sounded in the discussion of chemistry and physiology and their prominent place in the psychotherapeutic picture might lead the reader to believe that (1) decreasing credence is to be given to the dynamic interpretation of mental disorders and (2) the future of psychological treatment is doomed. Neither conclusion could be further from the truth. The normal functioning of mind and body has been regarded for years, even centuries, in the light of psychological functioning. The dynamic approach, be it Freud's, Horney's, Jung's, or that of some other acceptable school, will continue to be used in the attempt to explain why and how we think while we are living physiologically, chemically, environmentally, spiritually, and culturally. Chemistry may analyze the bodily ichors to the nth degree; physiology may delineate metabolism and glandular secretion. But how the psyche works and responds to these will always be understood and interpreted in the dynamics of psychology. Psychiatrists generally agree that when a person is sick, no matter what is going on in his blood vessels, nervous system, or bodily organs, he is beset with unconscious fears of death, and the most potent antibiotic is not going to drive these fears from his id.

That a symptomatic panacea may some day bless psychiatry is very possible and even quite probable, but will it succeed in removing the patient's reaction to emotional conflicts? Will it help him to solve his life problems? A patient may seek medical aid for persistent headache. A physician can prescribe analgesic medication which nullifies pain as long as the patient continues to take the medicine. However, not until the *cause* of the headache—faulty vision, sinus infection, and so forth—is discovered and removed, will the headache cease and the patient be able to abandon the medication. This same type of situation has prevailed in psychiatry for some time: a depressed patient will have his melancholia relieved by electric shock therapy; the administration of ataractics (tranquilizers) will make a difficult patient manageable; but these methods actually only alleviate symptoms. Psychotherapy now takes over, and probes for the underlying causes. If this latter step is unqualifiedly successful, a clinically complete "cure" can be claimed. But if the psychotherapeutic step is not taken, there is every likelihood that the depression or another emotional or psychic disturbance will recur.

4: Everyday Tensions and Anxieties

"Transient situational personality disorders," the first category listed in Chapter 2, represents the starting point in the ascending scale of severity in mental disorders. In this group one finds the temporarily disturbing reactions which most of us have experienced in our everyday brushes with various life problems. The junior executive who has missed an elevation to a vice-presidency may feel the sting of disappointment, mope about at home nursing the wound to his ego for a while, and then bend his efforts to meet the challenge of qualifying for the next opening. The young girl who is jilted may weep unconsolably for a week, then reconstitute herself for a new amorous adventure.

It can be said that these are merely "run-of-the-mill" examples of average behavior, hardly eligible for psychiatric consideration, and this would be a reasonable appraisal. With some individuals, however, the reaction to the same type of problem would be very strong and, for a time, incapacitating; for such people simple psychotherapeutic counsel, which may be all that is needed, should be sought. Should the reaction persist or threaten to become more severe, consideration must be given to the possibility that a more profound emotional disorder or a severe mental reaction is present, in which case the need for regular and intensive therapy will be indicated.

Transient situational personality disorders provide excellent examples of the challenge in distinguishing between "normal" and "abnormal." The civil servant who fails a competitive examination and is "down in the dumps" for a week or two may present no real psychological difficulty. But what if he fails to snap out of it? In other words, how brief or how long is "transient"? At what point do we conclude that his response is too intense or too protracted, his adjustment deteriorated—that is, when is it "abnormal"? The best available yardstick is a comparison of the individual's post-situational personality with that which existed prior to the troublesome event.

Anxiety and tension are probably the commonest sources of disturbed mental equanimity. The broker who watches frantically as the ticker tape unfolds the story of his financial disaster is anxious and tense. So is the mother of the young soldier crouched in some far-off foxhole, as is the son himself, who faces the very real danger of enemy firepower. Anxiety, which gives rise to tension, is an essential of life, almost as necessary as hunger and thirst. Without the capacity for anxiety the individual would lack the ability to recognize and react defensively to the various incidents and people that threaten him in many ways throughout life. Anxiety (a conscious expression of unconscious fear) and tension (a mobilizer of the individual's mental and physical forces for defense against real or imagined threats) are basic, indispensable self-protective reactions.

According to Dr. George S. Stevenson, consultant to the National Association of Mental Health, everyone experiences tension in appropriate circumstances, and this tension is greater at some times than at others. While an occasional bout of anxiety and tension may be unpleasant, it is quite normal and need not be cause for concern. Indeed, it may be beneficial. When Edison was trying to create the electric light he failed in one experiment after another. He could, with each failure, have become dejected, disgusted, and imbued with a sense of futility to the point of abandoning his project. However, *anxious* to consummate his dream and spurred on by *tense* preoccupation with his work, he made successive attempts, missing meals, sleeping no more than three hours a night, until he created the first electric bulb.

It is everyday anxiety and tension, then, that drive so many of us to strive for accomplishment, to reach for perfection, to better that which is already good. They are the emotional motivating forces behind persistence and determination. Anxiety and tension are periodic expressions of the emotions of the performer about to step out on the stage, of the applicant approaching an interview for employment, of the individual on his way to the "daily double" window at the race track, and of the physician at the bedside of a coronary victim hovering between life and death.

When do these situations just described, giving rise to anxiety and tension, become "abnormal"? The time to be watchful is when emotional upsets, which accompany excessive tension, begin to occur frequently; when they shake the individual severely; and, above all, when they fail to wear off after a reasonable amount of time (after the precipitating factors have subsided or disappeared). Dr. Stevenson has prepared a list of questions for the individual to ask himself when anxiety and tension make themselves felt. The questions follow, with explanatory remarks by this author.

1. **Do minor problems and small disappointments throw you into a "dither"?** Consider the housewife who plans the following day's chores in timetable fashion, with a "tight" schedule. If a telephone call should delay her or the washing machine break down, the prospect of temporary failure may be too great to bear. Such a woman may become hysterical, disorganized, and frantic, rushing wildly from task to task, actually accomplishing nothing. She has fallen apart at her "emotional seams."

2. **Do you find it difficult to get along with other people and are people having trouble getting along with you?** Here we have the "griper." While the first part of the question is his real trouble, he invariably expresses it in terms of the second half. *He* isn't out of step with the world; the world, he claims, is out of step with *him*. There is at least one in every shop, office, club, congregation, or other group. Suppose all the machinists have agreed to rotate week ends, which would be fair for all. But not to Joe's mind. When his time comes to show up, he pleads for an exchange; it's always the "wrong week end" for him, and his repeated attempts to juggle the schedule, his irritability and his sulkiness upon being rejected, make it impossible for him to adjust democratically in his occupational milieu. His resentment spreads to every phase of his job. He becomes the slacker, the conniver, the selfish smart aleck. His feelings are always hurt, and he savagely blames everyone but himself for what is really his own maladjustment. His is a budding paranoid personality.

3. **Do the small pleasures of life fail to satisfy you?** When Mary goes out with a boy friend, she is perfectly satisfied with a walk along the river bank, watching the boats and enjoying a stimulating, thought-provoking conversation. Susan, on the other hand, dreams of the Golden Horseshoe, opening nights, the Stork

Club, and a sojourn on the Riviera. If her escort provides her with nothing more than a movie and a soda, she is dissatisfied. It is not unusual for us to respond to the lure of indulgence beyond our means, but well-adjusted individuals, retaining their sense of values, find it possible to turn their heads from unattainable luxuries. Others, not so well-adjusted, tend to go in for unnecessary display (e.g., paying excessive rent for a showy address when it is not practical to do so, or squandering an entire week's salary on one evening at a night club). Such persons are prey to feelings of insecurity; they can feel secure only when in possession of material things, and the majority of them go through life "missing the boat."

4. **Are you unable to stop thinking about your anxieties?** This is the person who is chronically anxious about his anxiety. His obsessive preoccupation precludes his adjustment to life's demands and challenges, not to mention its pleasures and harmonious interpersonal relationships. He is the chronic neurotic who foolishly delays seeking clinical help.

5. **Do you fear people or situations that never used to bother you?** "I'll tell you, doctor, I used to enjoy teaching but for the past few months I find the kids are getting on my nerves. I can't concentrate. I'm irritable toward everyone." Does this sound familiar? We are all acquainted with the person who seems to be "losing his grip," who is not so efficient as he once was, whose emotional behavior shows that he is succumbing to overwhelming feelings of inferiority and inadequacy. Such individuals are often seen in the changing years (see Chapter 13). Those who have remained stationary (in career, in family development, in cultural evolution) while their fellows have progressed, have more than an unconscious realization of the threat from youthful competition, of the waning of the energy and efficiency which they enjoyed earlier in life. What once were ordinary tasks are now "too much for them." They eye with dread the pall of empty, unemployable old age, of being unwanted—an ominous threat that easily provokes chronic and deepening worry, insecurity, and tension.

6. **Are you suspicious of people, mistrustful of your old friends?** Much that was said under Question 2 applies to this type of person whose actions are defined by the term "poor interpersonal relationships." Some factor or factors—trauma, neglect, mistreat-

ment—may have narrowed his emotional activities to an eye-for-an-eye way of responding to life. Such an individual is "from Missouri"—every statement must be substantiated. He lacks the warmth of camaraderie. Eternally suspicious, he interprets a legitimate appeal for charity as the "trick of a crooked syndicate." All athletic events are "fixed," and every gift is a harbinger of some favor which the donor will eventually request.

7. Do you feel inadequate? Do you suffer the tortures of self-doubt? Somewhat in the sense of Question 3, here again one finds the individual with unconscious feelings of insecurity. He is indecisive, wishy-washy, irresponsible, and constantly plagued by misgivings about his ability to complete the simplest assignment or to make the most uncomplicated choice. These are the complaints which the psychiatrist most often hears from the individual who lacks self-confidence and self-reliance. An example of this type of person is the man or woman who writes a short social note only to tear it up and rewrite it—again and again.

If your answer to any of these questions has been "Yes," do not jump to the conclusion that you face emotional disaster. It would, however, pay you to undertake a reappraisal of your attitudes and behavior. Dr. Stevenson offers the following simple, practical suggestions.

Talk it out. If you are worried about something, don't bottle it up. Select some levelheaded person whom you can trust and take into your confidence—husband or wife, brother or sister, parent, close friend, your pastor, the family physician, a teacher. Bring the problem out into the open and "kick it around"— what psychiatrists call "ventilation." It will provide you with a fresh viewpoint, an unprejudiced opinion, and will relieve your emotional strain. It will permit you to see your worry in a clearer light, perhaps even to cast it off entirely.

Escape for a while. This is not meant as advice to "run away" from a situation. A brief change, in the full realization that return is imperative, may be the best immediate response to an emotionally painful experience. This short escape, in which you may lose yourself in a movie, a concert, a sports event, or a week-end trip, can be most helpful. It has the same basic philosophy behind it as the sudden recess declared by a judge in a tense trial, as the industrial "coffee break," or "the pause that refreshes." The masochistic type of person who forces himself to stand and suffer subjects himself to needless self-flagellation; he discovers "the hard way" that his problem remains unsolved. Bear in mind that when you do "escape for a while," you must be prepared to come back and deal with your difficulty. You will have no excuse for avoiding the issue when you are composed and in a better condition emotionally and intellectually.

Work off your anger. This is not to suggest that you should give way to unbridled expression of your anger in tantrums and destructive behavior. Reacting with rage to psychological pain, frustration, and disappointment is irrefutable evidence of a person's immaturity and is an infantile method of dealing with difficulties. It solves no problems, wins no friends, and may leave you feeling foolish and repentant. There is, in fact, psychological validity in the adage, "Count to ten first." Restrain today's choleric outburst and make your calm reply tomorrow. Meanwhile, think the problem out, take a long walk, play some game, pitch into some physical activity.

Give in once in a while. It's a hundred-to-one bet that you can't be right all the time. The person who is chronically involved in quarrels, who is unfailingly obstinate and defiant, is the adult reproduction of the thwarted child who rages and screams, "I won't! I won't!" When you are convinced that you are right, there is no harm in standing your ground, but even in this situation it is not *what* you say, but the *way* you say it. Oftener than not, it is the soft answer and the calm attitude of self-assurance that will go further in convincing your adversary of your knowledge of the subject of the argument. But even when you are "dead right," try turning the other cheek from time to time. You will feel better for it, and it will win you the reputation of being broad-minded; it may induce others to yield occasionally, too. Above all, this sort of approach to controversy will discourage the building up of tension and will give you a sense of satisfaction and maturity.

Do something for others. Are you exclusively concerned with yourself? When someone starts to "weep on your shoulder," do you hear him out, or do you launch into a recital of your own tale of woe? The latter reaction is an indication of excessive egocentricity. Develop the habit of doing something for someone else now and then. It will help to take the sting out of your worries and, what is far more significant psychologically, will give you the warm feeling that comes from assisting a fellow human being.

Take one thing at a time. This advice applies to two types of individuals. First, there is the "eager beaver" who apparently seeks to impress others (and himself) by tackling everything in sight at once. In this category one finds the Christmas shopper who dashes up and down department store aisles, plunging toward "men's neckwear," only to pass "sweaters" and be distracted by a particularly good-looking item, scattering his efforts without plan, and failing in the long run to accomplish his purpose. Secondly, there is the anxious individual who, in confronting a new work load, regards it as so monumental he just cannot get started in any part of it. Unable to separate the wheat from the chaff, incapable of determining what is urgent and what can be postponed, he ends by getting next to nothing done. One way to overcome this impasse (that of the shopper as well as the worker) is to ask yourself, "Am I not overestimating the importance of what is facing me?"

Shun the superman urge. Here we have the perfectionist, who castigates himself into a state of anxiety because he believes that he is not accomplishing as much as he should. In aiming for the moon, he actually invites failure. He has a constant feeling that his work is incomplete, unsatisfactory, and of low caliber. An honest inventory and appraisal of one's personal assets are indicated. Decide what the things are that you do well and concentrate your efforts on these; they will probably be the things that bring you the greatest satisfaction anyway. Do not demand of yourself perfection in everything you do.

Go easy with criticism of others. As common as weeds in a garden are the employers or supervisors who set themselves up as paragons after which subordinates are expected to model themselves. A top sergeant may have an innate capacity for working at a fever pitch and will feel that every man in the squad should act likewise. The "man in the squad" may be a spouse, a child, or a pupil. Avoid the tendency to force other people into the pigeonholes of your own set of standards. Bear in mind the wide range of individual differences among people. But if you find this difficult to do, at least put a damper on your urge to criticize in an aggressive manner. Interpersonal relations are not improved by desk-pounding, shouting, or sarcastic references to the failings of others.

Give the other fellow a "break." Condescension, mere tolerance, and patronization—these will not do. A "break" implies more than the spoilsport who ill-naturedly and grudgingly gives in. There is no one more tense and anxious than the person who, trying to compensate for a feeling of inferiority, feels the constant drive to "get there first." He is the motorist who grimly and compulsively must "beat" the car ahead, then the car ahead of that, and so on. As in the case of the schoolroom bore who must get more "gold stars" than any other student, life becomes an endless race for first prize. Such an individual eventually "runs out of breath" emotionally, and someone suffers as a result. Happiness never follows this attitude toward life. Admittedly, competition is contagious, but so is co-operation.

Make yourself available. Often we find ourselves feeling that we are "left out" when there is no justification for this attitude. There are people who turn down one invitation after another to participate in community activities and then, when some especially desirable activity comes along and they are not included, they insist that "people don't like them." This drives them further away from wholesome interpersonal relations. Instead of shrinking away, withdrawing, and stewing in the juice of your self-pity, it would be far healthier to make yourself available, to make overtures on your own. There is, of course, a middle ground between withdrawing and "pushing." Try it.

Schedule your recreation. In a world of shorter work hours, long paid vacations, and daylight saving time, it is a sad commentary on human existence that we frequently fail to take the time, even when given the opportunity, to relax. The person who just "can't take time out" should deliberately set up a rigid schedule of hours for recreation. It is emotionally cleansing to submerge oneself in an absorbing hobby and forget all about work. The vacation is an annual event used as the occasion for doing something pleasurable for which one does not ordinarily have the time (even the vacation is too often undertaken with the unrelaxed vigor of a Crusader); but what of the rest of the year? While it is true that "all work and no play makes jack," it also makes anxiety and tension.

Emotional difficulties frequently arise out of practical problems such as financial status, trouble on the job, parent-child relationships, and marital difficulties. These, as was said before, are precipitating factors. Just as often, the individual's long-standing habits and attitudes may produce conflicts. These interacting forces within and without (i.e., endogenous and exogenous) tend to accumulate, and each serves to aggravate the other. If too much of this process has gone on, we may need more help than we can give ourselves, help of the sort available at a counseling or guidance service. Such assistance may be obtained in family welfare agencies, schools, churches, industrial plants, and settlement houses. Trained counselors can help to clear up the more practical and immediate aspects of the problem.

If, however, an emotional disturbance of a transient, situational nature becomes too distressing or lasts too long, it should be dealt with as an illness requiring professional treatment, just as one deals with a cold when it becomes too severe. Consult your family physician. He may recommend that you visit a psychiatrist, he may suggest treatment at a clinic or mental hospital, or he may resolve your problem on his own. It all depends on the severity of the condition.

The quest for peace of mind (which is synonymous with good mental health) is universal, but few of us are blessed with all the internal qualities and external circumstances that will guarantee it. We must work for it. This means striving to obtain a better understanding of ourselves and others. It also implies working out our life problems by ourselves when we can, and being wise enough to know when we need competent help. Above all else, we need a basic philosophy of faith—faith in the ability of people to improve and grow; faith in the desires and capacity of human beings to work out differences co-operatively; faith in spiritual and moral values, and in the essential decency of mankind. Faith of this sort will carry us through many stressful situations that might otherwise shatter us.

5: *Psychosomatic Illness*

The neurotic reactions that emerge as a wide range of "physical" ailments (stomach ulcer, irritable colon, coronary disease, and many others) have been reserved for discussion in this separate chapter because of the role they have played in the evolution of a significant viewpoint in the practice and philosophy of medicine: the holistic concept. This idea emphasizes the inseparability of emotional experience and bodily function. Whereas the orthodox organicist maintains that "there is no function without structure," and dismisses as window-dressing the neurotic patterns of behavior, the holistically minded physician insists that if it were not for mental and emotional experiences, structure would have no function other than keeping a biological machine in motion. Since he is never called upon to treat a simple biological machine, but an extremely complex subject—a human being beset by fears, anxieties, and frustrations —the holicist feels compelled to look beyond tissue changes and laboratory findings for both etiologic and therapeutic indications.

The notion is not entirely new; psychologists and physiologists, as well as philosophers, have wrestled with the mind-body problem for ages. Until recent years, however, medicine, while it was willing to leave the most obvious "nervous" disorders to the specialty of psychiatry, insisted on the primacy of organic factors in the diagnosis and treatment of a wide gamut of physical illnesses, now regarded as possessing a strong psychic (or emotional) element in their causation. Token gestures, it is admitted, were made in the general direction of psychotherapy in the vague form of homespun bedside psychology, couched in such phrases as "Avoid excitement and worry," "Take it easy," and "Get your mind off business." The preoccupation with pathology evolved out of Pasteur's discovery of "germs," and medicine was dominated by the microscope and test tube; trivial lesions revealed at post-mortem examinations were frequently used to "explain" a disease. While this cause-and-effect dictum was a forward step in science, it was not necessarily the outstanding medical achievement of the time. The dramatic and radical change in thinking came about when Walter B. Cannon, father of endocrinology, developed his thesis of the "wisdom of the body," which underscored the need to recognize the influence of both learned and unlearned "drives" as factors affecting physiologic processes. It remained for World War I to bring into bold relief a large number of "body-mind" disorders—conditions in which the presenting symptoms did not fit into the neat, pigeonhole categories established for lesions of the nervous system.

By 1940, so impressive an amount of evidence had been amassed in clinical (chiefly nonpsychiatric) records, that it was no longer possible to ignore the role of the mind in the causation of certain disorders whose chief observable symptoms were organ pathology and dysfunction. By this time, too, the specialty of endocrinology had come into its own and served as one of the determining factors in closing the gap between psyche (mind) and soma (body). This was accomplished by demonstrating that emotional disturbance can upset hormonal equilibrium, which in turn can bring about dysfunction in a target organ.

With rare exception, contemporary medicine subscribes to the tenet that psychic factors predispose the individual to a host of bodily disorders and malfunctions. The concept of disease has been broadened to include "psychosomatic" ailments. But even this comprehensive term is thought by some authorities to imply a dichotomy between mind and body, and for this reason they prefer the term "holistic medicine."

THE MECHANISM OF THE PSYCHOSOMATIC CONDITION

While it is not possible to determine how much is psyche and how much is soma in any instance, clinical studies indicate that mind influences body far more significantly and frequently than body influences mind. Just how the interaction takes place is not easily explained. The brain has emotional centers which are linked to other brain centers and to the endocrine glands. These centers serve as way stations for the emotional changes which are then relayed down the spinal cord and via the nervous system to blood vessels, muscles, mucous membranes, and the skin. The emotional centers in the brain also seem to act as "condensers" of emotional changes accumulated through previous experiences. The close interweaving of the nervous and endocrine systems with the functioning of the organ systems of the body ensures that the harboring of anxieties and frustrations cannot fail to have reverberations in organ dysfunction somewhere in the body. To what degree serious pathology will develop is, of course, an individual matter.

THE BODY AS A MEDIUM OF EXPRESSION

As pointed out earlier, the most common psychosomatic disorders are associated with the gastrointestinal tract. It has long been recognized that stressful interpersonal problems which cannot be resolved by the mind are "taken on" by some other part of the body. When an irritating friend or a troublesome member of the family cannot be coped with, the patient becomes "ill." There are very real alterations in the digestive tract of the person who remarks that he cannot "stomach" a situation, or that someone "gripes him." An individual who suffers a bitter disappointment that "sours" him on the world, may very easily be victimized by excessive stomach acidity. These verbalized homologues of feeling were referred to by Edward Weiss and O. Spurgeon English as "organ language." Physicians have long known that the cause of such gastrointestinal disturbances is an emotional conflict—a clash of attitudes with desires. Until recently, however, there was little or no therapy with which the physician could "reach" such patients, for two reasons: (1) effective therapy would be time-consuming and (2) doctors generally experience difficulty in formulating therapy of this sort in terms that are both understandable and acceptable to the patient. Enlightened as we may have become in matters of mental hygiene, most patients shy away from the suggestion that their "physical" illness may have an emotional (mental) background. The all too frequent retort is, "You mean there is something wrong with my mind?" The increased tensions of our life have, however, brought to the fore so many illnesses which are unresponsive to traditional treatment that it is high time for everyone to understand the dynamic relationships between body and mind; even greater progress could be achieved if more people appreciated the actual oneness of the two.

A man who feels inadequate or inferior may, with the help of his mind (but by an unconscious process), create a socially acceptable excuse for his failure. This externalized apology takes the form of a "physical" illness. Military medicine provides the most striking examples. The G.I. Joe whose unconscious demanded surcease from fear of death during a prolonged assault against the enemy could not stop in his tracks and scream, "I'm scared! Get me out of this situation!" True, when his ego-censorship was weakened he may have done just that, but, in the vast majority of instances, when the individual could not consciously control his fear, safety had to be obtained in a manner which his milieu would tolerate. Consequently, in order to satisfy both his unconscious desire to flee and the demands of social opinion, our soldier had to solve his mental problem through his body. He became paralyzed, suffered cardiac palpitations, or developed colitis. For his emotional salvation and the preservation of his ego, the physical disorder was a necessity. And so it is with many harassed souls whose anxieties are generated by less imminent dangers than those of the battlefield. As in the case of the psychoneuroses to be described in Chapter 6, a compromise situation is established—the physical illness.

There are, on the other hand, many well-adjusted persons who apparently survive all manner of emotional problems without ever having recourse to physical illness. Indeed, they may not even show outward indications of pathological processes to which they are prey: it is not uncommon for physical examination of an elderly patient to reveal evidence of previous severe heart disease; autopsy studies of old persons who died of illnesses other than, say, coronary disease, have shown heart scars indicating that they had been "stricken" years before without overt symptoms! Owing to their excellent emotional adjustment, such individuals afflicted by heart disease had no need for the "satisfaction" of the bodily handicap and consequently did not suffer the classic cardiac attack.

WHAT CAN THE DOCTOR TELL THE PATIENT?

When a person is suffering distress he will want to know why. He will not be satisfied with attempts to reassure him that pain is "only" psychic in origin. Often enough, he does not need a physician to tell him this, because his associates at home and at work may have reached this conclusion through daily contact with him and have probably remarked to him, "It's all in your head." What the patient does need is a friend who will explain to him the interplay of emotional and physical forces, and this friend should be the person best qualified to impart that information accurately—a physician.

It is a common lay belief that all pain originates from a direct cause—broken bones, bruises, cancerous growths, inflammations, and infections. In other words, discomfort is regarded as coming from something that can be seen (by examination, X-ray, or laboratory findings). However, it is widely known that physical distress can, and often does, result from factors which cannot be seen. For example, in the wake of fear the mouth becomes dry, blood vessels are constricted, and blood supply, as well as glandular activity, is reduced. The "sinking" feeling in the pit of the stomach experienced in "stage fright," and the dryness of mouth of a person called upon to make a public address, are common physical symptoms. Laboratory investigations have demonstrated that, under emotional stress, glandular activity in the mucous membrane and various other parts of the gastrointestinal tract decreases. Changes in muscle tone of the digestive system may result in severe cramps.

Another example of the arousal of pain in response to emotional changes is the fact that, under stress, the diameter of blood vessels in the cranial cavity increases, and the stretched tissues around the vessels exert pressure on the nerve endings, resulting in what is known as a "nervous" headache.

In short, in an emotional crisis, no part of the body is exempt from physical discomfort traceable to a change in one or more of these three elements: (1) blood nourishment, (2) glandular functions, or (3) muscle tone.

The many common superstitions about disease and illness do not result because "a little knowledge" is dangerous in itself, but rather because "a little knowledge" may cause the individual to draw conclusions about his condition which may lead to much anxiety. The following popular misconceptions will indicate how many people with minor discomforts or ailments readily consider themselves seriously ill:

Any pain in the left chest means heart disease.
Pain after meals or a pain in the stomach means ulcers.
Pain in a joint must mean arthritis.
Pain in a muscle is due to neuritis.
Pain in the head probably means a brain tumor.
Every lump is a sign of cancer.

Many persons cannot bear to suffer any kind of pain or discomfort. They seek an absolutely painless existence, in which the occurrence of any discomfort signifies danger. In spite of repeated medical counsel that they are perfectly healthy and that there is no physical explanation for their distress, they persist in their anxiety and earnestly seek a doctor who will corroborate their traditional ideas.

TREATMENT OF PSYCHOSOMATIC ILLNESS

When the patient's history, physical examination, and laboratory tests show no evidence of organic pathology, but indicate that emotional problems are present, the doctor's exposition of psychotherapy may begin somewhat in this fashion:

"Your chief concern is pain and distress in the stomach (and/or bowel). We know that a healthy body functions painlessly and since yours does not, and all examinations were negative, it is highly probable that the disturbance may be traced to emotional difficulties. Let us consider, for a moment, how the rhythm of bowel function is laid down and how emotions can upset it."

The physician proceeds to describe the normal muscular movements of the digestive tract as being rhythmic and flowing from mouth to anus. He then tells how, under certain conditions, this smooth action becomes irregular, reversed, or otherwise perverted. Irritants to the lining of the stomach will produce discomfort and vomiting, in the same manner as the toxins (poisons) of infections. Emotional conflicts can produce these effects also, and such symptoms can be as prolonged and severe as those caused by any other irritants.

The physician may continue: "Early in infancy, there is a direct relationship between the stomach and the emotions as the child's main physical and emotional needs are felt. This relationship persists in later life, and often adult behavior can be traced to and explained in terms of early experiences. Moreover, the mind and the stomach are so intimately connected through the nervous system that, when the mind is incapable of handling a particularly formidable task, and anxiety and insecurity increase, the stomach takes over and tries to vomit out the unpleasant situation—a *rejection* of a painful or distasteful emotion which cannot be mastered in any other way. Thus, for a time at least, emotional weakness in the face of a given problem is obscured behind a curtain of physical illness."

Most of us are aware that discomfort does not necessarily indicate that disease is present. Under stress, the psyche creates emotional impulses which alter physiological function; *the patient must understand this point,* because one of the therapeutic objectives is to dispel the patient's preoccupation with his bodily discomfort. This does not mean that the physician can pass lightly over the problem of pain for regardless of its emotional basis *the pain is real.* Much harm has been done by the curt remark, "Your pain is purely imaginary." The patient expects the doctor to explain the *reasons* for the pain or discomfort while he discusses the diagnosis. Even after a comprehensive physical examination the patient will not be satisfied with "I find you healthy in every respect," or "I do not find any evidence of disease in your case. You have nothing to worry about." (Nothing to worry about —when the very foundation of the illness may be worry!) Contrary to logical expectation, symptoms are not eliminated when the patient is informed he is free from organic disease. The emotional disturbance that underlies the discomfort is not a logical mechanism. Often it arises from complex life experiences in conflict with strong id drives. A clinical brush-off by a "hard-boiled" physician will only drive the patient to another doctor in search of the answer to the problem. This "shopping around for a physician" is a common practice among neurotics. Many such patients could be helped with psychotherapeutic council, leavened with understanding humanity. Admittedly, some are entangled in a baffling network of frustrations, anxieties, and fears; for them, a fuller psychiatric program of treatment is needed.

In the course of explaining the mechanics of emotions and how they affect blood supply, glandular activity, and muscle tone, the physician can uncover and discuss the emotional problems and attitudes which are producing the distress of which the patient complains. He will help the patient to re-experience the conflicts which triggered the perverted physiological activity. The anxiety, anger, and feeling of inadequacy will be felt all over again, and through this "playing back," the patient may be able to talk, scold, or otherwise drive them from his mind. The unconscious, free of its emotional burden, will no longer *need* the outwardly manifested physical illness—the compromise selected by the distraught ego in its attempt to satisfy the unconscious and the demands of society. Once the skeleton is out of the closet, the house is no longer haunted.

6: The Deeper Tensions and Anxieties— Psychoneurosis

The term "psychoneurosis," which designates the deeper tensions and anxieties, has yet to be satisfactorily defined. The dual nature of the word—*psyche,* mind + *neurosis,* disorder of the nerves—implies that there is some kind of pathology present (i.e., something has "broken down") in the structure or the mechanical functioning of the nervous system. The popular term "nervous breakdown" implies that a pathologic condition is present. There are, to be sure, a few clinical entities in which this is true; in medical parlance these are known as "neurologic disorders." Their cause is clearly demonstrable as a lesion in the brain and/or nervous system, which may be a congenital flaw, or the result of injury or disease. To further complicate the issue, the term "neurosis" is also commonly accepted in the psychiatric vocabulary as a synonym for "psychoneurosis."

In his approach to a better understanding of the psychoneuroses, the reader will find it helpful to recall earlier references to the difficulty in distinguishing between "normal and "abnormal." In the realm of the deeper tensions and anxieties, this problem comes to the foreground. As the psychiatrist Abraham A. Brill stated: "Freud showed that the difference between hysteria (a type of neurosis) and schizophrenia (a psychosis) was only one of degree. Soon thereafter he demonstrated the same relationship between the neurotic and the so-called normal person. In his *Psychopathology of Everyday Life* he showed that many ordinary faulty actions—mistakes in talking and writing, forgetting, misplacing things, and other common errors—are all due to unconscious emotional disturbances, and as such show the same distortions as do neurotic and psychotic symptoms. . . ."

In short, Freud demonstrated that there is no such thing as a trivial mistake, that is, a mistake without a reason for its occurrence.

With this problem of sorting out "normal" from "abnormal," it is necessary to stress the importance of the cultural milieu in the evolution of a neurosis. Indeed, the very foundation of Karen Horney's approach to "the neurotic personality of our time" is her declaration that "a neurosis is a disturbance in one's relation to self and others." Behavior is often regarded as normal or abnormal (neurotic?) on the basis of where and when it takes place. Secret fraternal initiation rites re-enacted in public would be unacceptable as normal behavior, however seriously they may be regarded in their appropriate setting. A shapely thigh accidentally revealed by an attractive woman boarding a bus draws the attention of every male within eyeshot, but the same woman parading practically nude at a beach resort may not earn more than a passing glance.

The age of the individual also affects our judgment of his deportment. The very young are permitted fantasy behavior for which their elders may yearn but in which they must not indulge —a small boy on a city street imitating a locomotive engine by emitting puffing noises and shuffling his feet causes no concern at all, but an adult who talks and gestures to himself in a crowded subway car is at least a source of discomfort to his fellow passengers.

CHARACTERISTICS OF PSYCHONEUROSIS

While the medical dictionaries, as well as many writers in the field, differ widely in their definition of psychoneurosis, there is general concurrence on the following points:

1. A psychoneurosis is a disorder of the mind (psyche).

2. Some psychoneurotic manifestations resemble those seen in neurological disorders.

3. In a psychoneurosis the disorganization of the psyche is only partial, in contrast to the total disintegration in a psychosis.

4. Ordinarily, the psychoneurotic individual has some insight into his condition; he recognizes the abnormality of his behavior and attitudes whereas the psychotic does not.

5. All the varieties of psychoneurosis are characterized by emotional manifestations of anxiety and tension.

In addition to those just mentioned, the accompanying table of differential diagnostic criteria outlines the major points of comparison between a psychoneurosis and a psychosis.

DIFFERENTIAL DIAGNOSTIC CRITERIA

Factors Under Consideration	Psychoneurosis	Psychosis
1. Dynamics (according to Freud)	Ego *vs.* the id.	Ego *vs.* the outer world.
2. Personality	Generally intact; only partially changed.	Totally disorganized; changed in whole.
3. Reality	Patient usually feels reality means the same for him as for the rest of the community.	Patient usually ignores or shuts out reality.
4. Mechanism of Projection	Conscious sense of guilt.	Unconscious sense of guilt.
5. Language	Unchanged.	May be disturbed, as in incoherence, irrelevance, or "neologisms" (new words).
6. The Unconscious	Is expressed indirectly.	Is given direct verbal expression.
7. Infantile Regression	Not present.	Reflected in behavior as, for example, unashamed soiling.
8. Affect and Thought	Harmony undisturbed.	Frequently not in harmony.
9. Flow of Libido	Outward to the world of reality (transference).	Inward to the self (narcissistic).
10. Object Attachment	Erotic: makes for strong object attachment.	Autoerotic: makes for weak object attachment.

As indicated by the above table, the psychotic person shuns the world as we know it and steadily regresses through the various stages of psychosexual development. In many cases he finally returns to his infancy, the period of his life when he enjoyed the utmost in personal security, safe at his mother's bosom and in her arms. Here one sees the classic picture of the schizophrenic: ripping off clothes, requiring bathing and spoon- or tube-feeding, and soiling himself. Finding gratification in this aura of complete irresponsibility, so characteristic of babyhood, the psychotic sees nothing worthwhile in reality; indeed, it may be so distasteful to him that he seeks surcease in suicide.

The neurotic individual, on the other hand, while he does not find fault with reality in general, is acutely aware of his conflict with his surroundings—the conflict usually existing within a closely circumscribed area of life problems, emerging as some specific anxiety or frustration. The neurotic, too, would like to return to a secure stage of his life, but he is barred from doing this by a well-developed, unyielding, ironclad superego which firmly informs his unconscious that society frowns on the "baby who howls for mother." A virtual *impasse* ensues; the relentless demands of the id for overt expression of the unconscious fear have clashed with reality's intolerance of such open expression. Escape from this *cul-de-sac* is accomplished by a "compromise" which satisfies social demands: a neurotic reaction. The anxiety and tension generated by the fear may be drained off through a physical illness, as seen in psychosomatic disorders. Because these conditions are the forms of neurosis most commonly encountered in clinical practice, they have been made the subject of a separate discussion (see Chapter 5). The other neurotic reactions or types of psychoneurosis include: anxiety reaction, dissociative reaction, phobic reaction, obsessive-compulsive reaction, and hypochondriacal reaction.

THE VARIETIES OF PSYCHONEUROSIS

Over the past few decades much of the terminology in the field of the psychoneuroses has undergone radical revision. Many of the older designations have been abandoned; the clinical entity "neurasthenia" has disappeared, and other terms which had been more or less loosely applied (such as "shell shock" from World War I and "combat fatigue" from World War II) have been dropped from general usage. Some psychiatrists have, in fact, insisted that any attempt to devise such descriptive labels for hypothetical "types" of psychoneuroses is time-wasting and does not enhance the therapeutic approach, which depends heavily on buried factors in the life history of the individual under treatment. Most of the clinical terms used in the past served only to describe the situation that precipitated the psychoneurosis, and they failed to touch on the psychodynamics involved.

Anxiety. The nature of a psychoneurosis can be fully appreciated only when the element of anxiety is understood. This emotional manifestation is the outstanding and most usual symptom or sign of a neurotic disorder. Anxiety is one of the few medical terms that covers a symptom, an affliction, and an emotional response. It is applicable, likewise, to both normal and pathogenic affective (mood) manifestations—the difference between these two being dependent upon the provocative cause, the time element, and the individual himself. Anxiety over the safety of a loved one who is serving in a combat unit during war is understandable. Continuance of that reaction following cessation of hostilities is questionable. Anxiety from without, i.e., precipitated by a real stress, disappointment, or challenge, is to be expected if the precipitating factor is proportionate to the apprehension. Anxiety from within, i.e., arising purely within the individual's mind, is definitely an indication of a psychic disturbance. It is currently accepted that the mentally ill person reacts to his unconscious conflict with fear, which, to the neurotic, is not a socially tolerated response; it is outwardly converted into anxiety as an affective presentation of instinctual drives. This apprehensive, worrying, troubled reaction consists chiefly of emotion and is surcharged with tension.

Psychoanalysts claim that instincts have ideational forms of presentation (i.e., ideas accompany each instinctive urge) and that, in the process of repression, the ideational expression of an instinct disappears from the conscious sphere, if it is there, or remains in the unconscious. Accordingly, three courses are possible for instinctual, ideational presentation: (1) complete suppression, (2) appearance in the guise of a particular type of affect (mood), or (3) transformation into anxiety. Many psychiatrists object to the ambiguous intermixture of anxiety and fear in clinical literature. However, there is little doubt that the former is an outward expression of inner, unconscious fear. Sigmund Freud postulated three situations which were almost certain to precipitate a later manifestation of anxiety: loss of a love object, the castration complex of childhood following a parental scolding or punishment for normal sexual curiosity, and the superego (conscience) or social fixation.

As an emotional expression, anxiety is commonly encountered in its maximal strength—intense, marked, and extreme. Its logical and psychic origins are well covered by Eugen Bleuler, who said: "Anxiety undoubtedly has different sources. In many cases it is plainly connected with respiratory difficulties as seen in diseases of the heart, in the respiratory organs, and in the blood. Furthermore, anxiety is undoubtedly connected in some way with sexuality, a fact which we knew for a long time, but which Freud made clearer."

Anxiety may be attached to definite thoughts or ideas; or it may exist without any ideational association, in which case it is referred to as "free-floating" anxiety. It is often accompanied by physical signs, such as short, rapid breath, accelerated pulse, sweating, and alternating flushing and pallor, all of which indicate a close organic-physiological association with the adrenal glands, the sympathetic nervous system, and possibly the subthalamic nuclei (emotion-controlling centers) in the brain. Investigators, particularly Jules Masserman, have been studying these interrelations through the use of fear-producing stimuli in laboratory animals.

Anxiety Reaction. Clinically, this is the commonest type of neurosis, in which the patient presents an overwhelming reaction manifested physically as diarrhea, urinary frequency, palpitation of the heart, tremor, insomnia, lack of appetite, or some other abnormality. He may sense an indefinable uneasiness, a feeling that he is facing imminent disaster (for example, a fear that the grim reaper is just outside the door, or that he faces social and economic ruin).

Dissociative Reaction. The individual's anxiety and tension may be so distressing to him that he manages to divorce himself from his own identity, for a time at least. One form of this reaction is a sort of Jekyll-Hyde paradox; one day the neurotic is thoughtful, calm, and solicitous; another day he is harsh, carping, hysterical, and demanding. The dissociation may, however, be so effective that amnesia or a fugue state is produced.

Amnesia. Amnesia (loss of memory) is readily feigned by persons who have run afoul of the law, but improved psychological tests (such as the Rorschach or "inkblot" test) have assisted greatly in differentiating shammed from true (neurotic) amnesia. Furthermore, piercing inquiry into the life history of the delinquent or criminal usually uncovers childhood clashes with authority, patchy school attendance, petty thefts, a poor work record, and previous arrests. Such features are usually missing from the life history of the neurotic; in their stead are found frequent episodes of illness, "nervousness," and so forth.

Fugue State. In a fugue state, the individual acts automatically —as if in a dream. He may run away, often traveling great distances from his home environment. When the fugue passes he cannot recall what has happened in the interim. Classical examples of this condition are to be found in the biographies of Vincent Van Gogh and Robert Schumann.

Delirium. This manifestation of many severe organic illnesses, such as delirium tremens in alcoholism and delirium in high fevers, is also seen in psychoneurotics. The patient is wildly excited, incoherent, out of contact with his surroundings, and may be hallucinated. Delirium, like amnesia, may be feigned.

Phobic Reaction. This type of neurotic illness was formerly regarded as a subdivision of "anxiety neurosis," but the latter term has long since been relegated to obscurity. Without fear human beings would be easy prey to many dangers. Fear makes them alert, and the emotional reaction of fright is, therefore, normal and necessary. But unreasonable fear, such as panic, which is pervasive and intense beyond the demands of the circumstances, can incapacitate the individual. The term "phobia" is applied to responses in which the threat of harm is usually remote and, to the majority of persons, not worthy of attention. There are many such phobias, which the reader will find listed in the Glossary of this book. Whether or not a fear is neurotic in character depends on several conditions. Is the fear justified —that is, does a real threat exist? Is the fear "selective"—is it only this one sphere or situation in which the person experiences fear? Does the tension generated by the phobia interfere with the individual's daily routine, his work, or his interpersonal relations? Some of the commonest phobias are: bathophobia (fear of falling from a high place), claustrophobia (fear of being in a confined space), necrophobia (fear of a corpse), agoraphobia (fear of open, limitless spaces), and photophobia (fear of bright light).

Obsessive-Compulsive Reaction. An obsession is a constant pre-occupation with a given thought or a complex of related thoughts, which the neurotic person cannot "shake." A compulsion is an irresistible urge to some kind of action, usually the physical translation of an obsessive thought. According to Freud, the background of the obsessive-compulsive reaction is ritualism —an ageless phylogenetic inheritance of man which is seen both in primitive societies and in contemporary civilization. In the latter, religious and fraternal rites are examples, but even more familiar in everyday life are such common responses as the phrase "God bless you!" following a sneeze. Examples of extreme, and distinctly neurotic, compulsions in mature individuals are the urge to memorize license plate numbers of passing automobiles and the attempt to avoid stepping on a crack in the sidewalk. This sort of compulsion was immortalized in the case of Samuel Johnson, who meticulously ran his cane over each picket of the fences he passed.

In the discussion of criminality in Chapter 9, the question of psychopathy versus neurosis is raised. The borderline is annoyingly unclear. Consider the arsonist, for example. He may appear as a plain, ordinary insurance-pilfering criminal, but, in reality, he may be a pyromaniac, driven by a morbid, compulsive drive to produce a conflagration. There appears to be a definite association between pyromania and arrest at the infantile level of psychosexual development, particularly in genital orientation (pyromaniacs have admitted getting a sexual "lift" from watching the destructive results of their acts). Once this sexual gratification has been achieved, the "firebug" is overcome with remorse, but when he next feels the urge to light a fire, he yields readily to the obsession.

A similar diagnostic challenge occurs in separating the neurotic kleptomaniac who obsessively steals, cannot deny the compulsion, and suffers an emotional conflict involving frustration of acquisitive desires, from the ordinary shoplifter who pursues his felonious activity solely for personal gain.

Hypochondriacal Reaction. The hypochondriac calls for little explanation. The pattern of endless complaints about both real and imagined pains and organ dysfunction is well-worn. Less appreciated is the manner in which the neurotic person uses his hypochondriacal reaction as an instrument for gaining satisfaction, usually in the realm of interpersonal relations. Here is Aunt Martha and her strategic "headache." When domestic upheaval presents itself, or when life "just seems too much," she has a sudden, blinding, incapacitating occipital pain. She must lie down, alone in her darkened boudoir with a basin of cool water, witch hazel, and gauze pads at the bedside. No bickering now, no noise. Everyone must move on tiptoe while Aunt Martha is "recovering." Is her headache shammed? Not at all. It is a real pain, perhaps as excruciating as that of brain tumor; and what is worse, it is relentlessly habitual. This lady's neurotic behavior threatens to, and often does, become the guide to, and standard of, domestic protocol.

All the hypochondriacal Aunt Marthas are therapeutically recalcitrant. They traipse in and out of physicians' offices, smiling and patronizing, condescendingly allowing examinations to be conducted and prescriptions to be written. They may even follow doctor's orders for a brief time, but the thought of being relieved of symptoms is unbearable to them. So it's on to another physician, perhaps to a surgeon, or (usually at the end of the road) to a psychiatrist. Many, however, are taken in by cultists and quacks, in a vain attempt to find a cure.

Death Wish. A decade or more ago much attention was given to a category of psychoneuroses which is no longer recognized under its earlier descriptive designation: *neurasthenia*. Its principal manifestation was fatigue, which led to the belief that it was due to some "weakness" of the nervous structure. Proof of such causation was, however, lacking, and the category was eventually discarded. Nevertheless, studies in industrial mental hygiene (e.g., those of Halliday in Scotland) showed convincing evidence that a large proportion of accidents and of time lost through illness can be traced to neurotic patterns of behavior in employees. It is, of course, recognized that the possibility of malingering is always present, but Halliday's studies revealed many examples of workers who repeatedly injured themselves seriously in spite of the most modern safety equipment and intensive instruction in safe work practices. Such persons are described as "accident prone." Neurological examination of these individuals fails to reveal any organic pathology. In a static sense, one might say that they are unusually susceptible to fatigue, which lowers their capacity for attention and their reaction time. More dynamically, however, it has been suggested that these persons unconsciously *wish* to be ill, *wish* to be injured. In its greater extension, this theory has been described as a *death wish*. Indeed, the psychiatrist hears again and again from neurotic patients that they feel they are "unworthy," "inadequate," "not fit to live." Frequently, repeated accidents "unavoidably" incurred, serve as reality substantiation for an inner feeling of futility. Deep probing into the life problems of these individuals invariably uncovers a strong, unconscious sense of guilt which carries with it an equally strong emotional desire for punishment. The accident is the outward symbolic realization of this inner complex of feelings. Paradoxical though it may seem, the complete fulfillment of this unconscious demand would be accidental death. The majority of psychoneurotics, however, are content with less than lethal gratification.

Conversion Hysteria. Hippocrates (460–359 *or* 377? B.C.), "the father of medicine," believed that nervous disorders occurred only in females and, therefore, attributed these emotional reactions to malfunctioning of the womb (Gr. *hyster*). He coined the diagnostic term "hysteria." Sigmund Freud gave psychiatry the phrase "conversion hysteria," to describe the symptom complex whereby an inner psychic conflict, socially unacceptable were it overtly expressed in its actual content, is permitted conscious release of tension through the soma (body) and is finally presented as a physical complaint or illness. Modern psychiatry, in a broader approach to this subject, prefers the term "psychosomatic" disorder (see Chapter 5).

Neurotic Depression. Sadness is a normal emotional response to a grief-provoking situation—loss of a loved one, defeat of one's country by another, etc. The mood is "adequate" if the cause for it is likewise "adequate." Abnormality enters the picture when a person is overwhelmed by melancholia for no apparent reason ("I feel very blue and can't tell you why") or when the reason for the sadness is comparatively trivial (e.g., "I've been grief-stricken ever since our team lost"). Another element of abnormality is pathologically protracted melancholia, formally known as "reactive depression." In such an instance time does not heal all wounds, and the afflicted person grieves for months or years, whereas the average individual would have returned to normal spirits in weeks. This is the widow who weeps and wears mourning for the rest of her life in masochistic, inconsolable grief. A detailed discussion of melancholia, particularly as a complication of the menopause, is offered in Chapter 14.

TREATMENT OF PSYCHONEUROSIS

A reasonable approach to the treatment of the psychoneuroses was established by E. A. Strecker and F. G. Ebaugh. Many years ago they pointed out that any plan of therapy must be elastic, for it is a serious mistake to treat neurotics by rote. No two personalities, life histories, minds, or emotions are the same. Further, the ego in each of us subscribes to the "me first" principle. Consider the man on his way to the operating room—object: appendectomy. The orderly tries to reassure him, "Dr. Jones is wonderful. He has never lost a case." "Sure," the patient retorts, "but there's always a first time."

Treatment, therefore, must be custom tailored. The line of therapeutic attack will be modified not only by the patient's characteristics, but also by the psychiatrist's personal assets and his experiences in handling cases of neuroses. Treatment begins the instant the patient enters the doctor's consultation room. Often it has been said that the doctor's attitude should be strictly impersonal. Fortunately for sufferers of neuroses such an attitude is practically impossible to acquire. Remoteness and imperturbable intellectual detachment may satisfy the therapist but the patient, too, will remain aloof and the treatment program will be stymied before it begins. What the sick and emotionally disturbed individual requires most is empathetic interest in his difficulties. Without emotional *rapport* ("transference") no therapeutic progress is possible. Without transference there can be no "free association." By the latter is meant a spontaneous association of ideas and thoughts during therapeutic interviews and talks when inhibitory factors are removed, so that when the patient speaks of his thoughts as they become spontaneously conscious, they are voiced with little or no rational or ethical criticism.

History Taking. The patient has a story to tell, and the therapist must hear it—all of it—threaded though it may be with inaccuracies, omissions, prejudices, appeals for sympathy, and exaggerations. The practitioner who brushes aside the frailties of his patient as superficialities runs the risk of ignoring some of the information most valuable to him in his therapeutic approach. The patient's story plays a more significant role in medicine than is generally recognized. In this regard, the words of Félix Martí-Ibáñez, editor of *MD,* bear repetition:

"The most revealing historical document on the medical progress of an epoch is not a list of its foremost figures or discoveries, but any clinical case history made by a conscientious physician at his patient's bedside. . . . This is the most authenic form of making medical history.

"The clinical case history fully reveals the concept of disease that prevailed in a given epoch and portrays the physician's search for the nature of the disease. In that search nothing has been so important as the advent of the *biographic* concept of disease, which considers it a dynamic process that develops across time in the patient's life, as against the ontologic concept, which considers disease as an autonomous entity endowed with a natural history.

". . . If the present . . . approach of treating the patient as a *whole* person is not enough to indicate its value . . . recall the intriguing assertion made by the Hamburg clinician, Arthur Jores, that of the two thousand affections known in human pathology, we know the etiology of less than half, these being precisely those that man has in common with [other] higher mammals. The rest, of which we know their pathogenesis but little or nothing of their etiology, are *specifically human* diseases. This means that in order to solve their etiologic secret we must have a greater knowledge of man. Hence the ever-increasing tendency to make of medicine *medical anthropology,* that is, knowledge of the human being living by that anomalous and painful way of life represented by disease." *

While the foregoing is intended to apply to all forms of disease, it is strikingly applicable to the psychoneuroses. Because these are compromises with the inner and external environments, extremely important will be the patient's family background, his early rearing, his social, occupational, and spiritual experiences

* Félix Martí-Ibáñez, "Disease as Biography" (editorial), *MD, The Medical Newsmagazine,* 2:11 (October, 1958).

(especially those prior to the appearance of neurotic manifestations), and the history of the emergence of the neurotic reaction pattern. This need not be accomplished in a rigid, formal structure of question-and-answer; in fact, it is better for the therapist to work gradually into the history by listening to the patient's own account of the nature of his symptoms. Often the neurotic person is tense, worried, and anxious to unburden himself, and he will obtain some measure of relief in being able to describe the troublesome symptoms. He wants to "talk himself out"—to "ventilate"—and he will find satisfaction in doing this later on, when supplying data for the various divisions of the history.

The patient's revelation of his history will not be a neat, orderly account. The information is seldom given in chronological sequence; the patient may dwell on some factor which later proves to be inconsequential in terms of the neurotic reaction; he may falsify data, consciously or unconsciously; or he may omit many of the links which, while they are factually trivial, are fundamentally significant elements in the total emotional framework. Usually the missing data have been repressed. The psychiatrist will recognize such omissions and may encourage the patient to fill in the gaps if this will not generate antagonism (and hostility) in the patient with consequent refusal to supply further information. Or the therapist may let it pass, knowing that at a later stage of the history taking the patient may uncover the repressed factors. Particularly vital in the life history will be the patient's account of his interpersonal relations (especially those with parents), for these repeatedly turn out to have a bearing on the neurotic reaction; they are not uncommonly the core of the problem.

The history of the neurotic reaction itself needs to be exhaustive. The patient is urged to assign a date for the onset of the neurosis (it is seldom the actual date). The setting, personal and environmental, which existed at the time is closely scrutinized. Each major symptom is reviewed in retrospect from the time of its first appearance, and the incidents as well as the patient's reactions to them are noted. He is encouraged to give his own opinion of the causative factors, and no clinical "holds" are barred. "I don't know" and similar responses are not allowed to pass unchallenged. This is *not* analysis, it is history taking; the therapist makes use of this early contact with the patient to obtain clues which will be valuable and which will influence the therapeutic program. Again it is necessary to emphasize that this procedure cannot be inflexible. Some neurotic individuals are less repressed than others, and in their cases the psychiatrist can avoid protracted probing at a future time by stimulating as many revelations as possible in the history-taking stage.

The Physical Examination. The second step in the treatment program must be thorough, drawing upon the ultimate in skill of the internist and the best available clinical laboratory services. There are at least three reasons for this: in the first place, important somatic pathology may be, and often is, uncovered; second, the examination itself, if it is a searching one, has a beneficial effect on the patient; third, the psychiatrist is placed in an advantageous and authoritative position for subsequent therapeutic management of the case. Secure in the knowledge that he has acquired of the patient's physical status, he will be able to weigh the subjective phenomena. For example, if the patient complains of pain in a given area, and there is no evidence of serious pathology, the psychiatrist will be able to place whatever transient pathology there may be in its proper perspective.

Orientation of the Treatment Program. While this, the third step in the therapeutic program, is chiefly the concern of the psychiatrist, the reader may wish to understand how the treatment procedure is now crystallized in a definite plan based on the information thus far obtained. The psychiatrist must answer several questions of his own: What is the *apparent* origin of the neurosis? What are the relative weights of the psychogenic, somatogenic, and environmental factors? Is the organic pathology serious enough to indicate hospital or sanitarium treatment? Is the neurosis of a type which should be analyzed, or would analysis other than on a superficial level do more harm than good? (It may be that the physician should limit therapy to simple explanation, persuasion, and suggestion.) Are the social-environmental elements serious and capable of preventing the patient from solving his problems? Are they capable of correction? If at this point the psychiatrist does not have satisfactory answers to these questions, he knows he must delve further into the unconscious mind of his patient.

The Authoritative Interview. In the authoritative interview the psychiatrist does not seek information; he imparts to the patient his conclusions about the dynamics of the neurosis. He attempts to have the patient understand the main issues: the need for correction of physical liabilities or for further probing of psychogenic factors. In the case of the latter, he will work out the situations with the patient so that the manifestations of the neurosis will be understood as symbolic expressions of unconscious anxiety and tension. When the precipitating factor is some purely social-environmental situation against which the patient is rebelling, the patient's interpretation of this problem may have become involved with his deeper anxieties. The psychiatrist in this case will help him to understand that the immediate situation is superficial, and should not be allowed to cause the patient to lose his perspective.

Intelligent treatment of the neuroses requires that every individual case be approached in terms of its causative factors, in such a way that stress is placed upon those factors which can be modified. Factors which cannot be altered are recognized as such and the patient is trained to tolerate them. This pattern is actually followed by the patient himself when he is undergoing formal psychoanalysis; in other therapy programs, it is the psychiatrist who has the patient follow this plan.

The Criterion of Insight. No neurotic should be told that he is "cured" merely because his presenting symptoms have subsided or disappeared. If he has not attained insight into the underlying causes of his neurosis, he will only fall into some other type of neurotic reaction as a "compromise." Several investigators have maintained that in a large number of cases the neurosis is the best possible adjustment the patient can make, and that he can only be helped to live in relative equilibrium. The psychiatrist must avoid making rash promises with regard to the possibility of recovery. Not only does this tend to alienate the patient (who may still be clinging to his neurosis as a life preserver), but he may fail to develop confidence in the psychiatrist if immediate improvement is lacking.

There is much more to be said about treatment of the deeper tensions and anxieties which impinges on the general subject of treatment of all mental disorders. In Chapter 8 ("Back to Mental Health—Treatment") will be found discussions of the following matters as they relate to the psychoneuroses: simultaneous treatment by psychiatrist and internist; tranquilizing drugs (ataractics); psychotherapy; psychoanalysis; hypnosis; and re-education.

7: *Flight into Another World—Psychosis*

From the contrast drawn in Chapter 6 between neurotic and psychotic reactions, the reader has gathered that the neurotic person is acutely aware of the troubled state of his personality and his behavior, but not, however, of the hidden elements, and his neurosis may be the best available solution to his difficulty. While he does not meet his problem head-on, he does make an attempt, however oblique, to resolve his anxiety in the sphere of reality. For the psychotic, however, the only solution appears to be flight into another world—a world of his own design which he can control. For him, the real world is too restrictive, too dictatorial, too unsympathetic, and insecure. Accordingly, the psychotic rejects this world and creates his own galaxy of associates and situations, in some cases even his own language.

REGRESSION

A significant feature of the psychotic's personality is its resemblance to the personality of babyhood. If, prior to the emergence of the psychosis, the individual has made a passable adjustment on an adult level, it must be assumed that he has *returned* to the infantile level—that is, he has *regressed*. It is this dynamic, psychological occurrence that determines what specific psychosis a mentally ill person will develop. If the prepsychotic personality is characterized by suspiciousness, a tendency to misinterpret the words and intentions of others, etc., the illness to be anticipated—if one is to develop—is that of a paranoid psychosis. If the personality is marked by mood swings ranging from elation to abject depression, a manic-depressive psychosis will be the future reaction.

By regressing, the patient retraces his steps to the protective shell of security which he knew in infancy. There, beyond the reach of society's limitations, he constructs his own, thoroughly satisfying world of fantasy, where he can rule supreme with the "magic omnipotence" described by Freud. The fantasy world of the psychotic is patterned after the experiences of his earliest years. This accounts for the psychotic patient's regression—speaking incoherently, soiling unashamedly, and requiring personal care and feeding, perhaps curled up in the corner of a room, hunched over in the "uterine position" which is the acme of regression. Reverting to behavior associated with the fabrications of childhood, he "sees" and "talks to" real, but nonpresent, or fictitious beings (hallucinations); he believes what he wants to believe, whether or not such beliefs are logical, feasible, or factual (delusions). Similarly, like the infant, the fully developed psychotic presents varying defects in his orientation, intellectual assets, responsiveness, and judgment; above all, he lacks insight. His thinking is "autistic"; that is, he is preoccupied with ideas that range from a mixture of fantasy and reality to complete exclusion of the real world.

The similarity between infantile and psychotic behavior has another equivalent—primitive life, where social custom is such that unrestricted comportment is characterized by personal gratification before consideration is given, if at all, to the group. Studies of aborigines reveal typical feral, childish, uninhibited practices. In Freud's notable work, *Totem and Taboo,* these three are calibrated equally: infant behavior, primitive thinking, and psychotic regression. How often is the unchecked child described as a "little savage"?

Furthermore, the aborigine, the infant, and the psychotic, each concerned with an egocentric drive to satisfy his own desires in a ruthless and swift way, is said to be "pragmatic" in thinking and action, after the "practical" philosophic concepts of William James and Charles Sanders Peirce. His thought or wish is directly executed in an action designed to gratify his immediate need, regardless of the consequences.

SOCIAL MALADJUSTMENT

Another, and very practical, consideration that distinguishes the psychotic from the neurotic reaction involves the capacity of the individual to move about on his own in society. The sufferer from a neurosis may be an infernal nuisance to his associates, and his eccentricities may interfere with his family relationships, his job, and his community activities. But he is usually able to "get through the day," cope with the average demands of the milieu, complete his work, and generally conduct himself in a manner neither threatening nor annoying to himself or to others in his environment. Ordinarily this cannot be said of the psychotic. As will be seen in the discussions of the psychoses which follow, his impaired judgment, his disordered interpretation of persons and events, and the serious disruption of his ability to communicate may lead him to behave in ways that may result in injury, destruction, and turmoil, or at least in confusion. The psychotic may lack interest in reality factors to the extent that he is unable to care properly for himself, his family, or his property. This has provided the basis for the legal attitude concerning institutionalization of a psychotic who requires this "for his own welfare and/or that of the community." When there seemed to be little hope for improving the lot of the psychotic person, much less "curing" him, the foregoing attitude was warranted on humane grounds. Recent developments in the treatment of these seriously incapacitating mental disturbances have, however, suggested that we might well revise our concept of the position of the mentally ill in the community.

It is not true that all psychotic persons require institutionalization. Some, whose conduct is not offensive or menacing and who create no personal or community problem by remaining in the environment, receive treatment at an out-patient clinic, a "day" (or "night") hospital, or in the office of a privately practicing psychiatrist. Likewise, thanks to rapid progress in contemporary therapy, more and more hospitalized psychotic patients are being released (and not too long after admission) to continue treatment on an extramural basis.

VARIETIES OF PSYCHOSIS

A psychosis may accompany or be due to several somatic afflictions: infections, poisons, injury, epilepsy, senility, arterial thickening, menopausal changes, brain tumor, endocrine disturbances, mental retardation, etc.

More commonly, however, a psychosis arises *sui generis,* as a "functional" process—i.e., with no discernible, tangible, or demonstrable organic pathology. The commonest types of functional psychoses are: schizophrenia, manic-depressive psychoses, paranoia, and paranoid conditions. Of these, schizophrenia accounts for most of the patients in mental hospitals. This mental disorder and the psychic afflictions of the aged are responsible for the institutionalization of two out of every three mental patients. It is the functional syndromes that have defied all efforts to establish specific causation, hence the qualifying adjective "functional."

Schizophrenia. This disorder was originally named "dementia praecox" by Emil Kraepelin, "the father of modern psychiatry," in recognition of one of the disease's principal characteristics, childishness in behavior and speech, which supported the notion that illness developed during early years, hence "dementia of the young." As accumulated clinical data and newer diagnostic concepts evolved, it became apparent that the condition often takes years before it manifests itself, by which time the victim is well into later life. This latter situation prompted the Swiss psychiatrist, Eugen Bleuler, to introduce the term "schizophrenia" which means "split mind." This descriptive term more aptly covers the nature of the symptoms and the patient's preoccupation with an unreal world, i.e., his "bodily" presence in society and his "mental" residence in the universe of fantasy —the "split personality." The reader is cautioned not to take the word "schizophrenia" too literally, since there is no intention to imply that the brain is separated into two components. For that matter, medical science still awaits conclusive evidence of any specific brain pathology in this disorder.

Schizophrenics are invariably asocial—sometimes antisocial— seclusive, "lone wolves," and introverted. Very early in their history they may have been precocious (hence "praecox"), keen scholars, "bookworms," exceptional students who were regarded as "geniuses" and who were always too busy to squander their time on social activities. Schizophrenic individuals may be sulky, withdrawn, retreating more and more from environmental life factors. Emotional giving is foreign to them; accordingly, their interpersonal relations are poorly maintained or nonexistent.

Schizophrenia includes several types of reactions, the commonest being: simple, catatonic, hebephrenic, and paranoid. A schizophrenic patient who has marked mood swings, not unlike a manic-depressive case, is often diagnosed "schizophrenic-affective disorder." Where there is clinical doubt as to whether a patient is neurotic or is schizophrenic, or where neurotic features are prominent in a schizophrenic, or where a neurotic patient seems to be heading for a frank schizophrenic psychosis, terms such as "pseudoneurotic schizophrenia" may be employed. The designation "schizoid" means "like schizophrenia." It should be remembered that the diagnoses of these psychotic reactions are purely descriptive. All types of schizophrenia may be characterized by hallucinations, delusions, aberrant ideas, bizarre behavior, unpredictable movement, intellectual deterioration, orientation defects, etc., in varying combinations and degrees. There is no fixed "rule" by which certain signs and symptoms are specifically or exclusively peculiar to any one type, and there is, as in most psychiatric categories, a "mixed" type, indicating a combination of the characteristics of two or more schizophrenic reactions.

SIMPLE SCHIZOPHRENIA. The simple schizophrenic is the individual who expresses his distaste for life by utter indifference and apathy. Nothing in his environment attracts or stimulates him.

CATATONIC SCHIZOPHRENIA. This disorder is marked by a "breakdown" (*kata*) in posture, i.e., muscle tone (*tonus*). There are several varieties, the extremes of which are known as "catatonic stupor states." The patient may have a suggestible or a negative response. In the former, he may exhibit *cerea flexibilitas* or waxy flexibility—his arm can be brought up over his head where it will remain from several minutes to as long as an hour. His language and movements may be constantly repetitious (stereotyped), examples of which are "echolalia" (the constant iteration of a word or phrase heard), and "echopraxia" (the continued repetition of a movement seen). The patient may, on the contrary, resist any manipulations or suggestions, actively or passively (both are examples of "negativism"). In an active response, the patient's behavior is impulsive; he may become belligerent, even to the point of attempting homicidal attacks or suicide. In a passive state, the patient may retain a fixed, bizarre grimace, lips closed and protruding ("schnauzkrampf"). He may remain immobile and mute, refuse food, and be inaccessible to painful stimuli.

PARANOID SCHIZOPHRENIA. This type of patient reacts to ever-changing, illogically associated delusions. He is outstandingly suspicious, withdrawn, disagreeable, unco-operative, defiant, antagonistic, and asocial. Often, there is evidence of repressed homosexual tendencies. In an interview the patient may be evasive; he may even refuse to answer questions or discuss his case.

HEBEPHRENIC SCHIZOPHRENIA The descriptive term hebephrenia literally means a "tired mind," symbolic of the patient's total indifference, apathy, regression, asocial manner, and complete disinterest in reality.

Manic-Depressive Psychosis. Also known as "cyclothymia" (cycle of moods), manic-depressive psychosis is a severe mental disorder the clinical indications of which are manifested chiefly in exaggerated emotional changes which may be abrupt or gradual in onset. The diagnosis has been made with less frequency in recent times because, without doubt, many manic-depressive disorders are early, emotionally charged manifestations of approaching schizophrenia. Paralleling the mood changes are changes in thought (as expressed in speech) and movement. The manic aspect presents the disorder in its "up" stage, characterized by increase, as it were, in the three areas of speech, movement, and emotion; in the depressive aspect, these are reduced. If one stage follows the other, the affliction is described as "circular." The following table explains the features of manic and depressive types:

MANIC		DEPRESSIVE
"push" or overproduction of speech; "wealth," "flight," and "leveling" of ideas	SPEECH	dearth of ideas resulting in underproduction of speech even to the extreme of mutism
elation, euphoria, exaltation, hypomania	EMOTION	sadness, melancholia (with or without agitation) to the point of suicide
hyperactivity, restlessness, etc.	MOVEMENT	hypoactivity, up to immobility

A syndrome with some features of both manic and depressive elements present at the same time is known as the "mixed" type.

Paranoia and Paranoid Conditions. The word "paranoid" has several applications in psychiatric nomenclature. This term and "paranoia" have crept into everyday parlance via television, radio, novels, and newspapers, and are now glibly, interchangeably, and often incorrectly used. The words (*para,* faulty + *nous,* mind) refer to a state of mind in which the individual is inordinately and unjustifiably suspicious of the intentions of others. It is a natural, almost reflex action to be wary of sycophantic flatterers, "neighborhood gossips," and Paul Bunyans, as well as to be suspicious of rumors, hearsay, and preachments that lack at least some assurance of reliability, substantiation, and truth. However, the same attitude (particularly when it is chronic and/or the dominant personality feature), directed toward everyone and everything, is patently abnormal when it is manifested without any justification or proof and is emotionally disproportionate to the circumstances.

PARANOIA. In several of the psychiatric clinical entities, paranoid features are noted. The mentally ill person of advanced age may believe that relatives are plotting to do away with him for his property; some schizophrenics express delusions that are chiefly paranoid in content. In these instances, however, the paranoid trend is believed to be incidental to the main stream of the psychosis. Paranoia *per se is* quite a different matter. It is a chronic disorder of insidious development, characterized by persistent, unalterable, systematized, logically constructed delusions. The paranoiac is unbearably smug, conceited in the extreme. He is possessed of a sharp perceptivity and over-all intellect ("has a mind like a trap"), and is thus able to defend his central theme of persecution against the most reasonable arguments and in the face of all evidence to the contrary. Naturally, there is a mistaken premise as the basis for his reasoning, but this assumption ("people are plotting against me"), the cornerstone of the whole edifice of his mind, is unshakable. The paranoiac is essentially narcissistic; the drama that he plays out in his disordered frame of reference, portraying forces that are hostile to him, and his failures, which he attributes to the mistakes of others, are a cleverly designed defense of his love object—himself.

Paranoia is a "rare" psychiatric entity—rare, because the patient seldom seeks treatment and because the persecutory trend is expressed and revenge sought in a socially acceptable fashion. The paranoiac meticulously watches his conduct; he bends over backward to avoid criticism. He is litigious, traveling from court to court as the revenge-thirsty plaintiff whose endless suit for retaliation is based on a groundless grievance.

PARANOID CONDITION. When the persecutory ideas are less organized, but ever expanding to cover all phases of life, the state is referred to as paranoid condition. The delusions are poorly integrated and are usually accompanied by others of reference and influence and by hallucinations. Unlike the delusions of the paranoiac, the expression of these psychotic elements is in terms of phantasy rather than of reality. Many authorities, with whom this writer agrees, believe that paranoid condition is nothing other than a synonym for paranoid schizophrenia.

SYMPTOMS OF PSYCHOSIS

The most serious barrier to progress in understanding the mechanisms and causation of the psychoses is the impairment of communication, which renders these patients more or less inaccessible. Indeed, the principal value of the ataractic drugs ("tranquilizers") has been their effect in breaking through this curtain to pave the way for psychotherapeutic efforts. It is precisely because the psychotic "draws into his shell" that the recognition and diagnosis of these conditions have had to be inferred from presenting symptoms and signs. Compare this situation with that of the arteriosclerotic person, whose circulatory disorder can be detected on examination, and with the psychoneurotic, who is in communication with reality and can therefore be "reached" through interview and discussion.

The Significance of Symptoms. In the psychoses, as in the psychoneuroses, and indeed as in all of human behavior, the characteristic attitudes and behavior of the individual are reflections of the past. When it is possible to establish contact with a psychotic person, the content and emotional tone of his hallucinations and delusions will be found to stem from early life trauma such as frustration, fear, guilt, and the like. With the same objective as Aunt Martha (of whom we spoke in Chapter 6) who resorts to a headache to control her surroundings, the schizophrenic patient weaves his delusional afghan to resolve his unconscious fears. The neurotic is conscience-ridden, and handling of his problem tends to be complex and symbolic; the psychotic, motivated by his dominant unconscious, is unconcerned with the requirements of the outside world. His behavior and expressed attitudes may also take on a strange, involved pattern of a symbolic nature. Usually the central theme is an infantile emotional equivalent—hence, the general agreement that this is a "regressive" process. It should be borne in mind that isolated symptoms of mental disorders are of no value in an attempt to understand a given case. To have meaning, they must be studied as part of the holistic pattern that makes up the psychotic or the neurotic person.

Symptoms are the overt manifestations of unconscious desires, drives, conflicts, guilt and inferiority feelings, frustrations, and resentments, which are, at best, compromises as modified by the superego (conscience) through the ego. Therefore, a symptom is a "symbol" of some aspect of inner mental life. The commoner symptoms are divisible into nine groups, some of which are purely descriptive of the patient's reaction to life's stresses.

(1) **Disorders of Perception.** Perception is the action of the mind by which it refers its sensations to an external object as their cause. It is to be distinguished from sensation, conception (imagination), and judgment (inference).

ILLUSION. An illusion is a false interpretation of a sensory image. This is not uncommon under certain circumstances, e.g., the well-known desert mirage of an oasis.

HALLUCINATION. A hallucination is a sense perception not based on objective reality. One or more of the five senses may be involved: auditory (hearing), visual (sight), gustatory (taste), tactile (touch), or olfactory (smell) hallucinations.

(2) **Disorders of Thinking.** We are able to judge a person's thinking through his use of language (including speech and writing) and movement. Thus we can determine whether a patient's speech is coherent, relevant, and orderly, that is, whether he avoids "flitting" disconnectedly from one subject to another. Does his thinking represent a "poverty of ideas," does it yield to suggestion, and is it logical in its progression and realistic in content?

DELUSION. A delusion arises without external stimulus and provides significant clues to the patient's problems—frustrations, feelings of guilt and inferiority, inadequacies, rejections, desires, etc. Delusions of "grandeur" are compensations for unconscious feelings of inferiority, inadequacy, or insecurity. "Self-accusatory" delusions arise from the failure to repress unacceptable thoughts and desires. Delusions of "persecution" arise from inner threats of unworthy desires and of troublesome and distorted aspects of the personality, outwardly projected as hostility coming from the environment.

IDEAS OF REFERENCE. These are the patient's beliefs that remarks and/or actions of others refer to him when such is not the case.

IDEAS OF INFLUENCE. Such ideas refer to the beliefs that unpleasant and painful forces are incapacitating, particularly in the sexual sphere. Common examples of ideas of influence would be thought control, telepathy exerted by others on the patient's mind, disability from outer space missiles, etc.

(3) **Disorders of Consciousness.** Disorders of consciousness or "awareness" imply defects in the individual's "clearmindedness." A patient may be confused, unable to grasp what is said to him because he is bewildered or disoriented. The degree of clearmindedness ranges from sharp awareness to confusion, through cloudy and hazy consciousness to the extremes of stupor and unconsciousness. These disorders include delirium, fugue, and dream state.

DELIRIUM. This is more than a disturbance of consciousness. Acute in onset and in its course, delirium is marked by aimless overactivity, bewilderment, disorientation, incoherence (or dreamlike thinking), hallucinations, and illusions. Delirium is noted usually in high fevers or in toxic states, notably alcoholic delirium tremens (the d.t.'s). (For a discussion of delirium in psychoneurosis, see Chapter 6.)

FUGUE. As in music, fugue means a flight, from reality or the established norm. The victim "runs away" literally and psychologically from his customary environment and, when restored to conscious realization, does not recall (like the victim of amnesia) what has happened or where he has been during the fugue. (The fugue state in psychoneurosis is discussed in Chapter 6.)

DREAM STATE, akin to delirium, arises from an inner mental source rather than an outer influence (fever or poison). The patient does not recognize his environment and, in response to hallucinations, may run away (*fugue*), may resort automatically to acts of violence, or may behave in a fashion diametrically opposite to his usual mode of living. Dream states are common in epilepsy (Van Gogh's later years serve as a classical example) and in certain neuroses.

(4) Disorders of Apperception. When a patient "pays no attention" to what is said to him, or fails to react to an experience—from an abnormal response to none at all—he is said to have disordered apperception. Apperception can be defined as the mind's ability to "recognize," appreciate, evaluate, and digest an experience. Involved in this mental process are both attention and thought. The psychotic patient who has defective apperception will not understand the simplest question, although he knows language and the meaning of words. He will not be able to react normally to usual experiences and situations arising from his environment.

(5) Disorders of Attention. These range from intense concentration, through distractibility, to complete inattention.

(6) Disorders of Orientation. Orientation is the relation of oneself to time, place, and people. A patient may not only fail to identify himself correctly in relation to these three factors, but he may also "confabulate" to the point of misidentifying persons who are well known to or intimately associated with him.

(7) Disturbances of Affect (Mood). The prime criterion in judging an individual's affect or appropriateness of emotional expression is his mood. When a person laughs, is the provoking stimulus a proportionately humorous one? The disorganized patient who expresses mirth in response to a grief-arousing situation is said to manifest "inappropriate affect." Usually, such an individual is laughing at something humorous arising from his own world of fantasy and is ignoring the sorrowful event in the world of reality.

Depression is seen, depending on the situation, in varying degrees of sadness and melancholia. (Neurotic depression is discused in Chapter 6 where anxiety and tension are also described.) Pleasurable affect ranges from normal happiness and joy through "euphoria" (a feeling of abnormal well-being), to "elation" and the smug, self-satisfied mood of "exaltation." The patient who, because of his profound apathy and indifference, fails to respond emotionally to either sorrow or joy is said to present an "inadequate affect."

PANIC. More than fear, panic is a product of protracted tension, climaxing in abject fright, an intense feeling of insecurity, and suspiciousness. It is characterized by a tendency toward projection and ego disorganization.

AMBIVALENCE. This disturbance results in contradictory and simultaneous feelings toward the same object. During an interview with his psychiatrist, a patient may speak of his mother, using the most endearing adjectives. However, further questioning may elicit a deep, unconscious hatred for the parent, of which the patient is not consciously aware. Ambivalence is not unusual in normal, everyday life. A person may express abhorrence for fraternities and lodges because of the 'childish' ritualism, and yet be a devout and faithful member of his church, participating enthusiastically in the fixed ceremonial protocol of the Sabbath service.

DEPERSONALIZATION. This disorder of mood is characterized by feelings of unreality and changed personality. The patient may say that he feels he is not himself or that he is dead. He may also feel that the outside world is unreal. Depersonalization is common in severe depressions, certain neuroses, and schizophrenia.

(8) Disorders of Activity. Disorders of activity are manifested in speech and movement and run the gamut from immobility and mutism to uncontrollable restlessness and an unbroken babble of words or sounds. Certain activities, sometimes described as "mannerisms," have a repetitious quality, exhibiting "stereotyped" attitudes and fixed patterns of speech or movement. Constantly maintained immobility is known as "catalepsy," and constantly reiterated speech is termed "verbigeration." While one patient may resist commands "negativistically," another may be so suggestible as to respond "automatically." Compulsive action, governed by an irresistible impulse and usually arising from an obsession, is described in detail in Chapter 6.

(9) Disorders of Memory. Memory requires three mental processes: the reception and "registration" of an impression; the "retention" of the impression; and the "reproduction" or recall of the impression. Mnemonic defects may present themselves in a chronological, orderly pattern, starting with the most recent events and retrogressing to earliest childhood—a "retrograde" loss. Or memory may vary from day to day, remote events being recalled at one time and forgotten at another, with intervals of complete and pellucid memory alternating with those of severe defect. The first variety is common in disorders of the aging process; the latter, known as "patchy" memory defects, is often seen in patients with hardened cerebral vessels. Of less importance than the signs and symptoms delineated above are a few others whose definitions can be found in the Glossary at the back of this book. Amnesia (loss of memory) is discussed in Chapter 6.

TREATMENT OF PSYCHOSIS

While the layman has largely abandoned the concept of a mental hospital as an "insane asylum," a place long on detention and short on hope, a certain offishness and suspicion prevail toward institutionalization. There are still many who synonymize hospital and prison, and speak of people being "put away." Dr. Leland Hinsie pointed out many years ago that "the first step in a patient's treatment is his admission to the hospital," that is, separating him from the environment in which his mental illness developed. Institutionalization of the psychotic patient brings him one therapeutic advantage that is not available in an out-patient set-up. This is the so-called "total push" program, an outgrowth of and logical sequence to the holistic appreciation of mental disorders.

A patient today is never referred to a hospital solely for "treatment of the mind," which usually meant a weekly interview with the psychiatrist. It is the aim of present-day therapy to return the patient to the world of reality, literally and psychologically. Every component of his total life must be included in the treatment program: his family, occupation, community, religion, recreation, and the customs and mores of his civilization. These are some, not necessarily all, of the factors involved in maintaining interpersonal relations.

Therapy in an institution is a twenty-four hour affair. What can be expected of a patient and what the patient can expect—in recreation, occupation, and other spheres of his hospital and treatment milieu—is not discovered fortuitously, although a certain degree of trial and error is understandably indicated. Tests (personality, performance, aptitude, etc.) and interviews to determine potential or actual interests and abilities are used by every participant in the program: psychiatrist, social worker, psychologist, teacher, the occupational and the recreational therapist, etc. This is known as "assay and inventory of the patient's assets." Testing is exploited to the fullest by the treatment team, and it may lead to interests and achievements the patient may never have had or acquired; it may well be the all important spark that fans the flickering flame of ego drive into a glowing fire of healthy, extraverted aims.

Such over-all treatment is not a hit-or-miss proposition, but is carefully scheduled so that each item dovetails with the others, be it recreation, occupation, tranquilization, shock therapy, etc. Similarly, such a program is not static. It is modified as progress or lack of progress demands. The object of treatment for psychosis is not merely the removal of symptoms and signs; the ultimate goal is to return the patient to at least the level of adjustment which existed prior to the onset of illness, or to gain for him the adjustment he may never have had.

8: Back to Mental Health—Treatment

In mental or emotional disorders, the search for a quick cure has proved fruitless. There is no pill, no injection, that can be administered which will bring the patient back to health overnight. The treatment of mental illness involves a therapeutic program based on individual needs, emphasizing the principle of holistic medicine. The program may be extended over a year or more, and several different therapeutic methods may have to be used to achieve satisfactory results.

In cases of mental illness, perhaps more than in any other field of medicine, the unpredictability of the individual, his personal outlook, and his emotional make-up, are basic factors for consideration in diagnosis and prognosis. In cases presenting identical symptoms, causes and treatment programs may be widely different, and the possibility for cure may be greater in one case than in another.

In addition to these fundamental difficulties, the patient, in his search for mental health, may find himself hampered in many ways: by suggestions from ill-advised friends and relatives; by his own psychic make-up and response to treatment; by unsatisfactory home or work environments; or by the occurrence of somatic illness.

The reader is therefore warned against leaping to conclusions about the efficacy of any of the treatment methods described in this chapter. Tranquilizers have a place in the management of mental patients, but they can never be regarded as a cure, and to use them indiscriminately is to court disaster. Psychosurgery has shown some remarkable results, but it is applicable to only a small number of carefully selected cases, and even then is employed as a last resort. Electroshock can be undertaken with profit only within the pattern of a planned, over-all therapeutic program and is effective only for deeply agitated depressed states. In every instance many facts must be uncovered about the individual patient, and the adoption of any method or combination of methods will depend on the diagnostic findings arrived at through a study of the patient's life history, laboratory tests, psychological examinations, and other procedures available to the psychiatrist.

THE THERAPEUTIC PROGRAM

A widespread, though waning, misconception of the treatment of mental illness is that it is the exclusive prerogative of the psychiatrist. That misconception has probably had something to do with the false notion that this specialist functions in an area apart from the well-charted, more objective paths of medicine, although he is actually a medical doctor first and a psychiatrist second. The psychiatrist of today would be the last to claim a monopoly on the therapeutic role in mental illness. While it must be admitted that psychotherapy, a procedure in which he has special training, is the predominant vehicle for returning the patient to mental and emotional health, it is a rare case in which some other medical discipline will not be brought into action. The general practitioner who is well schooled in psychodynamics is in an excellent position to detect, prevent, and treat, within limits, the emotional problems of his patients. The particular knowledge and skill of the neurologist, surgeon, internist, endocrinologist, or other specialist are indispensable in instances where the malfunctioning of some body system or systems plays a part in either the cause or effect of the individual's disturbed state. Finally, working in fields tangential to the medical profession, but rich in contributions to the treatment program for mental illness, are the psychologist, social worker, occupational therapist, psychiatric nurse, and ward attendant—as well as the educator, the clergyman, and the volunteer worker. However, the more serious the problem, the greater is the need for a treatment program guided by a skilled and certified psychiatrist since by training and experience he is best qualified to treat the whole person.

Mental illness can be approached therapeutically on two levels —the psychologic and the nonpsychologic. The emphasis in the first case is on *psychotherapy,* but this word should be reserved for that phase of a treatment regimen which is planned and carried out by the psychiatrist. Certain environmental forces brought to bear upon the patient will also have a "psychologic" effect, but they do not constitute psychotherapy *per se.* For example, the social worker, under direction of the psychiatrist, may guide the patient's family in ways that will help the patient to adjust to his home and work milieu; this can be regarded as a "psychologic" aspect of the over-all therapy scheme. The term "nonpsychologic" denotes any of the modalities that are directed toward the soma or body: chemotherapy, dietotherapy, shock therapy, and others, which may be described under the inclusive term "the organic approach."

THE ORGANIC APPROACH

Not every case of mental or emotional illness requires residence in a psychiatric hospital or deep probing by a psychiatrist. The organic approach may be the sole answer to the problem. The lethargy, dullness, and indifference seen in one suffering from hypofunctioning of the thyroid gland may call for nothing more than administration of thyroid extract. In illnesses arising from endocrine gland disorders, such as inadequate or excessive activity of the pituitary, pancreas, or the adrenals, and in the manic (excited) and delirious features of pellagra (a condition that is due to vitamin B deficiency), the symptoms disappear when the indicated dietary corrections take effect.

Marked improvement in a patient's mental and emotional state can also be produced by rectifying deformities and physical handicaps. The depression of a deaf person gives way to brightness and cheer when a hearing aid brings him any discernible sound; the victim of a paralytic stroke, bitterly resenting his incapacity to earn a livelihood or even help himself, will surely look at life more optimistically if rehabilitation measures "put him on his feet again." Admittedly, the foregoing examples do not touch upon the more serious mental or emotional states such as those which occur in a neurosis or psychosis, but they do point out the benefits to any mental patient from some improvement in his physical condition.

Organic approaches directed more specifically to the alleviation of the mental or emotional distress have been receiving more and more attention in recent years. One that has taken on several forms can be described best as stimulating therapy; another term for it is "shock" therapy.

Stimulating ("Shock") Therapy. Over a span of several centuries, attempts have been made to "shock" the patient out of his delusions or hallucinations, his depression or excitement. Celsus in the sixteenth century used camphor; Hurd in 1885 tried a monobromate salt of the same substance; and a wide variety of mechanical means were employed which were little short of physical tortures. In France during the eighteenth century, patients were taken out of doors on the coldest days and sloshed back and forth in icy water; elsewhere, they were strapped in a chair and rotated (possibly on the theory that centrifugal force would cast off the disturbing element). Fifty years ago attempts were made to stimulate stuporous patients with carbon dioxide on the premise that this chemical compound, when present in excessive amounts in the body, excites respiration which in turn increases cardiac activity and consequently all of the body's metabolic processes.

Modern psychiatric "stimulant therapy" dates from Manfred Sakel's introduction of insulin shock in the mid-1930's. For paranoid and catatonic schizophrenics it proved effective but its general use was not substantiated. Clinical improvement, encouraging at first, was not maintained, and remissions were not uncommon. A patient who had been returned to coherence, stability, and fairly good contact with reality fared badly when he was placed in the environment in which his emotional disturbance had been precipitated. Nor did *metrazol shock* (metrazol is a camphor-like preparation) establish itself as a dependable therapeutic implement. Further, the risk was great in these treatment methods: the deliberately induced coma of insulin shock brought the patient dangerously close to death, and the more violent convulsions from metrazol introduced the serious risk of fractures.

Unquestionably, *electric shock therapy* (E. S. T.) is the simplest and safest of any of the shock therapies. It is indicated in cases of manic-depressive psychosis, involutional psychosis, and some forms of neurosis, and it may be given in selected cases of schizophrenia. The best results, according to Dr. Lothar Kalinowski who introduced this modality to the United States in 1940, are obtained with patients suffering from overwhelmingly agitated depressions.

In E.S.T., also known as "electric convulsive therapy" or E.C.T., the usual procedure is to place the electrodes on the scalp at the sides of the head. Mouth pads are inserted posterior to the incisors immediately prior to the application of the current. An ordinary household electric current is passed through the electrodes and, as a rule, a convulsion follows at once. In some cases there is an incomplete reaction of the petit mal type. Should this occur, a second application of the current is promptly made. When tranquilizing drugs proved effective in the management of mental patients, E. S. T. began to disappear from the treatment program.

Hormonal Preparations. In the field of chemotherapy, physiologists have been investigating the effects of certain hormonal preparations as psychiatric adjuvants. The basis of this work is the theory that the lack of hormonal equilibrium creates a metabolic defect in the nervous system and that this is manifested as a mental or emotional disorder. (Similar thinking has also generated an interest in the use of histamines, which originate from a protein.) One cannot doubt that there is a link between the emotions, the nervous system, and hormones. For example, the reaction to shock stimulates the sympathetic nervous system, and this causes the adrenal glands to react with increased hormone secretion. This physiologic activity is reflected in a flushed face, staring eyes, perspiration, and other outward manifestations, all of them forming a psychosomatic response to emotional stress. Why then would not these symptoms, seen chronically in an emotionally disturbed person, respond favorably to specific therapeutic measures in which the hormonal secretions were influenced? For example, radioactive iodine promptly controls goiter (a condition resulting from a hyperactive thyroid) by reducing the pulse rate and blood pressure and by alleviating symptoms of excitement (nervousness) and of exophthalmos (protrusion of the eyeballs). Similarly, antihistaminic agents have been useful in the control of asthma and similar afflictions which are partially caused by emotional factors.

Still in the test tube stage are the efforts to find a chemo-therapeutic agent which can be produced synthetically. Much work has been done with studies of hallucinogens (drugs which induce hallucinations) in the hope that their "counterparts" may be found—drugs which will oppose whatever process gives rise to bizarre thinking and thus place the patient in better contact with his surroundings.

Ataractics (Tranquilizers). For hundreds of years natives of India have been allaying apprehension, tension, and anxiety by chewing the herb *Rauwolfia serpentina*. From this herb have been derived the ataractics (tranquilizers) known as reserpine, serpasil, raudixin, and rauwolfia, as well as other preparations bearing trade names. On another chemotherapeutic front, a synthetic ataractic, thorazine (also called chlorpromazine, promazine, etc.), was produced in France. These two great advances ushered in the era of tranquilizers at the mid-century mark.

In the words of the researchers, tranquilizers are not considered to be the "final answer in themselves." They do not "cure"; nor do all patients respond favorably to them. There can be unfortunate side effects, too, such as Parkinsonism, skin eruptions, and the commonly expressed complaint of "dopiness." What the ataractic agents do is calm agitated patients without putting them to sleep, and render supposedly "hopeless" patients accessible to further therapeutic effort by reducing their anxiety and tension and by removing the "iron curtain" between the patient and those who seek to bring him back to mental and emotional health. The therapeutic relationship between psychiatrist and patient is noticeably improved because transference (described in detail on p. 53) can more easily take place and there is opportunity for a more productive free association.

A significant beneficial result from the use of ataractics in the treatment program has been the conversion of the atmosphere of the average mental institution into one more like that of the general hospital. Isolation rooms, mechanical restraint, continuous-flowing tubs, and the disturbance created by "violent" patients, even the familiar locks and bars, are no longer the trademarks of mental hospitals and sanitariums. Moreover, ataractics have helped to encourage the setting up of psychiatric services or pavilions in general and proprietary hospitals. This is a most wholesome outcome, for it indicates the emergence of.

psychiatry as another hospital division comparable to pediatrics, medicine, surgery, etc. Judicial commitments (or "certifications") are vanishing rapidly, as more and more patients or their relatives make application for treatment on a "voluntary" basis—as one would seek treatment for any other kind of illness, without prejudicing one's civil rights.

It is a fact that the most satisfactory results with tranquilizers have been obtained with the most disturbed patients who were "ward problems" for years, exerting a demoralizing influence on other patients. Another type of patient, up until now beyond the reach of the psychiatrist because of mutism, regression, and apathy, co-operates with psychotherapeutic efforts, and takes an active interest in recreational and occupational facilities, in his fellow patients, and, above all, in his personal appearance and hygiene. An unanticipated but welcome development has been the economic advantage of savings in heretofore gouged-out walls, smashed windows and furniture, ripped bedding and clothing, and the expense of extra personnel to manage the disturbed patients.

THE PSYCHOLOGICAL APPROACH: PSYCHOTHERAPY

There has been much controversy over the objectives in psychotherapy, with strongly expressed opinions about the inadequacy of mere "symptomatic" treatment. It is felt, for instance, that simply to remove the earmarks of a mental illness (odd behavior, response to delusions or hallucinations, and so forth), without getting at the roots of the disturbance and giving the patient insight into the causes of his emotional disorder, serves only to scrape away moss which will grow again. Yet it must be conceded that immediate attention has to be paid to the presenting signs, and no headway will be made toward the goal of understanding and long-term adjustment until the patient is rendered accessible to psychotherapy.

This view is best expressed by Leland E. Hinsie under "the objects and means of psychotherapy." He says, "Psychotherapy is adequate when it enables the patient who had previously enjoyed good health to regain his preclinical status through the complete removal of symptoms. This can be achieved with *children* by (1) removing unwholesome stimuli, or (2) detachment of their interest from earlier harmful habit patterns. In adults, psychotherapy attempts to remove symptoms by (1) building up latent or unused assets and (2) enlargement of interests in the environment."

The evolution of psychotherapy as an approach to mental and emotional disorders is extremely well explained in *MD,* the medical newsmagazine:

"The most vivid link between concept and therapy in medicine shines through the history of psychotherapy. The ancients observed that mentally ill people seemed to lose control over their actions: *ergo* some other force must be moving them, some incorporeal being. For the Biblical sages, insanity was an act of Jehovah and only divine intervention could effect a cure. For the pedantic scholastics of the Middle Ages, the mentally ill were possessed of the devil, for which the surest remedy was burning.

"In the so-called Age of Reason (18th century) it was still believed that the insane were sinners who must be locked away from society; it required the courage of a Philippe Pinel (1745–1826) to impose a more humane view of insanity as an illness. He equally pioneered in affirming that the origin of mental disease lay in pathologic changes in the brain itself.

"The history of psychiatric therapy until modern times included every manner of shock treatment: cold baths, rotary 'spits' to induce a semicoma, ascending douches, and a plethora of drugs to reduce the 'phlogistic' dear to Broussais.

"In modern times, organic therapy in psychiatry passed through intensive experimental therapy: induction of fevers, arsenicals, insulin coma, electroshock, injection of air in the cerebral ventricles, prolonged sleep, hypnotherapy, cerebral surgery. Concurrently, the psychoanalytic method sought for the cause of neuroses and psychoses in infantile psychic traumas or in the inability of a patient to adjust to the 'slings and arrows' of life.

"More recently psychotherapy passed into what some term the physiodynamic phase, searching for the cause of mental illness in a metabolic imbalance that causes a breakdown in communication between various parts of the nervous system.

"The present-day approach to mental therapy is organicistic and threefold: temper the severity of symptoms through such drugs as tranquilizers, establish better communications between patient and psychiatrist, search for the biologic causes of mental disease." *

Psychotherapy is effective when it enables the patient who has never experienced behavior, feeling, and thinking appropriate to his age level to *gain* (in contradistinction to *re*gaining) a pattern of reactions commensurate with the level of maturity he should have attained. This is best accomplished by removing or modifying the inhibiting factors which have blocked the individual's personality development. Such factors may be either endogenous (arising from within) or exogenous (arising from without). It is widely recognized that unwarranted guilt feelings are significant in this respect. Karl Menninger points out that therapy should provide a means whereby the patient can expiate guilt, find opportunity for creative expression, be given a chance to live out his fantasies, to establish advantageous attachments and suitable identifications, and, most important, to find love. One of the underlying principles of the psychotherapeutic effort is a recognition of the need for penetrating analysis of the psyche, thus making possible the release of emotions from earlier ideational and behavioral patterns. Only after this has been achieved can the patient's emotions be directed toward sublimated forms of activity.

Two complementary lines of action are involved in the psychotherapeutic process. At first it is analytic (taking the psyche apart); later on it becomes synthetic (putting the components of the psyche together again). Examples of the former are psychoanalysis and other intensive forms of individual psychotherapy; of the latter, suggestion and re-education.

In the broadest sense, psychotherapy is the effort to influence the attitudes of the patient—his attitude toward his own mental and physical processes; his attitude toward his environment, especially the people in his life; and his attitude toward his illness (degree of "insight"). The patient profits from psychotherapy when he begins to understand what makes him "tick"—when he realizes the nature and cause (or causes) of his emotional disequilibrium. His improvement will never be anything but superficial and probably transitory if he does not learn to recognize what factors and forces lie behind his mental illness, whether they

* "Disease and Man," *MD, The Medical Newsmagazine,* 2:68–75 (October, 1958).

are deep within his psyche or have been generated by faulty physiologic functioning.

Psychotherapy obviously cannot "change" a person's instincts. It can, however, alter the flow of unconscious impulses arising from the instinctual drives. Through a skillfully planned and conducted program of psychotherapy the patient's instinctual tendencies may be redirected to include *new* objects, as follows:

THE NEW FAMILY UNIT. In the patient-therapist relationship, the patient's emotional force is rerouted from the parent or other member of the family group to the psychiatrist, nurse, or attendant.

SHIFT OF LIBIDO. Mentally ill people are nearly always egocentric, wrapped in a sac of their own problems and their own importance. In the psychotherapeutic process the subject-libido is shifted to the outside world (object-libido) in large measure through "socialization"—presenting the patient with opportunities for group activity.

AROUSAL OF CREATIVITY. The patient who cannot be induced to participate in group activities may react favorably to recreational or occupational pursuits which put less strain on interpersonal relations.

There is no one unfailing approach to psychotherapy, for not only does each patient require a "custom-made" treatment program, but the individual patient's needs may vary as time goes by. Nevertheless almost all psychotherapy rests on the principles expounded by Sigmund Freud, whether the therapist uses the precise technique he advocated or one of the modified forms. It is therefore entirely reasonable to separate the psychotherapeutic methods into three categories: formal (Freudian) psychoanalysis; non-Freudian psychoanalysis; and other schools of psychotherapy. Psychotherapeutic adjuncts such as hypnosis, psychodrama, etc., must also be considered.

FORMAL (FREUDIAN) PSYCHOANALYSIS

In orthodox Freudian psychoanalysis, the patient reclines on a couch with the analyst out of his line of vision. The patient (the "analysand") is told to talk of anything that comes into his mind and his words are recorded by the analyst either in writing or by a mechanical recorder. Seldom does the analyst interrupt the patient. This process of producing otherwise suppressed material from the unconscious, called "catharsis," makes it possible for the analyst to be on the lookout for *indicators*—slips in speech and conduct which may furnish him with clues concerning the nature of the hidden difficulty. It is not a guessing game, nor is it a "third-degree" grilling. From the very beginning the patient appreciates the objective, because the psychiatrist advises him that the procedure seeks to probe the unconscious in an effort to uncover material which he cannot possibly bring to awareness in an ordinary interview situation. From Bergson comes the following explanation of the nature and purpose of the unconscious:

"For our duration is not merely one instant replacing another; if it were there would never be anything but the present—no prolonging of the past into the actual, no evolution, no concrete duration. Duration is the continuous progress of the past, which grows into the future and which swells as it advances. And as the past grows without ceasing, so also there is no limit to its preservation. Memory is not a faculty of putting away recollections in a drawer or of inscribing them in a register. There is no register, no drawer, there is not even, properly speaking, a faculty, for a faculty works intermittently when it will or when it can, whilst piling up of the past upon the past goes on without relaxation.

"In reality, the past is preserved by itself automatically. In its entirety, probably, it follows us at every instant; all that we have felt, thought, and willed from our earliest infancy is there, leaning over the present which is about to join it, pressing against the portals of consciousness that would fain leave it outside. The mental mechanism is arranged just so as to drive back into the unconscious almost the whole of the past, and to admit beyond the threshold only that which can cast light on the present situation or further the action now being prepared—in short, only that which can give *useful* work. At the most, a few superfluous recollections may succeed in smuggling themselves through the half-open door. These memories, messengers from the unconscious, remind us dimly of what we are dragging behind unawares. But even though we may have no distinct *idea* of it, we *feel* vaguely that our past remains present to us. What are we in fact, what is our *character,* if not the condensation of the history we have lived from our birth—nay, even before our birth—since we bring with us prenatal dispositions?

"Doubtless we think with only a small part of our past, but it is with our entire past, including the original bent of our soul, that we desire, will, and act. . . ." *

This is, perhaps, the most definitive expression of the concept of the unconscious component of the mind. Naturally the character and amount of expository detail which the psychiatrist provides for the patient must be gauged to suit the intelligence of the individual. In addition to being told the aim of the analysis, the analysand must be made to realize clearly that the treatment is going to consume a great deal of time and that he is not to expect advice or assistance concerning outside difficulties encountered during the period of analysis. Reports that a psychiatrist "told me to get a divorce" after two or three sessions are made out of whole cloth. After all, it is not the day-to-day problems, large or small, that the therapist is after, but the repressed material in the patient's past.

The usual treatment periods of forty-five to fifty minutes a day, five or six days a week, will take up several months, often a year or more. Treatment is completed only with an understanding of the final interpretation, and its success lies in the application by the patient of the new knowledge he has obtained.

Three techniques are available to the psychoanalyst: *free association,* already alluded to on p. 53; *word* (or *"controlled"*) *association,* responses by the patient to a prepared list of words; and *dream analysis.* The last can prove to be the critical phase of the analysis, for it may not only indicate the amount of progress made but may control the entire therapeutic program.

Dreams were regarded by Freud as realizations of unconscious or conscious wishes. What the dreamer recalls when awake is termed the "manifest" content, which was derived from the "latent," repressed material and molded into a form acceptable to the dreamer's ego. This is accomplished by such "mechanisms" as *condensation* (the dreamer merges the characteristics of several persons into one); *displacement* (he replaces the disturbing idea

---

* E. A. Strecker and F. G. Ebaugh, *Clinical Psychiatry* (New York: McGraw-Hill Book Co., Inc., 1935), pp. 579–580. By permission of the publishers.

with a more or less innocuous one); *secondary elaboration* (the transformed material is fitted together to constitute a more or less homogeneous dream story); and *symbolization* (the dreamer inserts events, persons, or objects as symbols for material which would prove embarrassing or injurious to his ego). This quite plausible account of the dream state is borne out by the incongruities and alarming episodes commonly reported in dreams and the difficulty (often the impossibility) experienced in giving a detailed, clear account of the dream in the waking state.

A critical point in analysis is the therapist's management of *transference,* which is manifested early by the patient and which is both a sign and a measure of resistance. In one sense, as Drs. Strecker and Ebaugh remark in their textbook on clinical psychiatry, "transference is the unconscious misidentification of the analyst, so that the patient may behave and feel toward him in a way which satisfied the experiences and impressions which refer to another." The measuring rod of the analyst, which in a way predicts whether or not an analysis will be successful, is the presence of the Oedipus complex. From its character and strength can be determined the potentiality the patient has for breaking away from the father or mother fixation and entering into a truly heterosexual life, that is, adjusting harmoniously to a world of men and women. More broadly, it is a gauge of the degree of adjustment to interpersonal relationships.

The final stages of Freudian psychoanalysis concern themselves with the overcoming of resistance, and the leading of transference by the analyst into safe and useful channels, so that when the analysand is ready for explanation, sublimation may be expected. We have previously defined sublimation as the outward expression of unconscious trends of interest through socialized and appropriate conduct. If sublimation is achieved eventually, then the cure is complete.

NON-FREUDIAN PSYCHOANALYSIS

Many psychiatrists follow schools of analysis other than that of Freud, although their techniques do not differ radically from those of the Viennese pioneer. Rather, it is the pragmatic concepts that follow somewhat different paths and thus influence the therapeutic approach to a patient's difficulties. The following are the leading analytical disciplines which, while they diverge from some of Freud's tenets, they also rely, to some degree, on certain of his fundamental principles.

Carl Jung. Although an early follower and contemporary of Freud, Jung developed a different concept of the human mind, particularly on the subject of the unconscious. The Swiss psychiatrist divided the unconscious into the *personal unconscious* and the *collective* or *racial unconscious*. The former is the repository of repressed ontogenetic experiences. These are within the life of the individual and may find conscious expression in dreams and in slips of the tongue. The collective unconscious is the phylogenetic (born of the species) heritage in which traces of experience, lived through ancestrally down the ages, are imprinted on the mind. Jung also gave us the terms "extrovert" and "introvert" to describe specific personality types, as well as the word association test, and he made many other contributions to psychiatry. He said that the "four basic functions of psychic activity are: *thinking* and *feeling*, which are rational and proceed according to laws of logic, and *sensation* and *intuition,* which are perceptual." Sensation perceives what is; intuition what may be.

Jung developed "analytical psychology" which emphasizes symbolism and religious beliefs as explanations of psychopathology (especially as it is observed in middle and later life) in terms of regressions to a collective unconscious or racial heritage. His later incorporation of Nazism into his theories cost him a great loss of prestige.

Otto Rank. Rank developed a system of therapy which emphasized transference (patient-therapist rapport) and the uncovering and "working through" of the anxiety precipitated "by being born." His course of therapy is limited to about ninety days. He was also interested in "incest motives" (disguised and undisguised) as unconscious provocations of personality disorders and emotional-neurotic reactions.

Alfred Adler. Adler placed more emphasis on the ego (self-preservative) instinct rather than on the sexual, and viewed psychosis as the result of conflict between the desire to dominate and a feeling of inferiority based upon some inherent organic defect. It is from this concept that Adler created the phrase "inferiority complex," which is so glibly bandied about at present. Adler pointed out that a man who has a definite defect (such as an impediment of speech) feels that this is his weak point and he therefore directs a surplus of energy in an attempt to overcome it. He may thus become a public speaker (like Demosthenes), or if he is unable sufficiently to conquer his feeling of inferiority he may become oversensitive concerning his defect, manifesting this through ideas of reference, i.e., that people notice it, or remark about it, etc., or he may develop a psychosis. The feeling of inferiority, Adler believed, has its basis in an inferior ego.

Regardless of the treatment discipline which the analyst follows, he cannot afford to lose sight of Freud's postulates. These are applicable to most analytic programs. The originator of psychoanalysis pointed out that the patient must present, to the analyst's satisfaction, a genuine, unconscious desire to be helped; the patient must be prepared to undergo analysis for a considerable length of time—perhaps years; he must have better than average intelligence; he must have sufficient financial means to be free of economic worries that might turn into resentment and suspicion directed against the analyst; and the patient should neither be a child nor a senile individual.

OTHER SCHOOLS OF PSYCHOTHERAPY

In spite of the universality of the basic Freudian principles, there are some disciplines whose approach to psychotherapy differs enough from that of formal psychoanalysis for them to be regarded as independent schools.

The foundation of the Freudian method—the belief in individualism and the constant struggle of man with his instincts—was modified as the impact of cultural environment on man gained attention. This shift of emphasis, brought about for the most part by economic developments, resulted in significant changes in the field of psychiatry. In addition to the complexities of drives within the individual, each person is to be recognized as a product of his environment; he has been shaped by his culture and, in large measure, is to be judged by the standards of his society. Sullivan and Fromm are the principal exponents of this "cultural" or sociological approach to psychotherapy.

Karen Horney. With her theory of "neo-culturalism," Karen Horney tried to modify a number of fundamental, Freudian psychoanalytic concepts. She focused her attention on cultural conflicts as the main source of personality disorders and stressed the principle of "basic anxiety," which, she felt, is a prominent factor in neurosis. She rejected Freud's libido theory, the significance of early psychosexual development and, in general, took a stand against genetic psychology in favor of culturalism.

Harry Stack Sullivan. While recognizing man as a basically biological organism, Sullivan stressed the importance of interpersonal relationships which affect the individual from birth and actually shape his personality throughout life. Sullivan's approach is both practical and flexible. His theory of interaction has particular significance for the analyst in the therapeutic program who must evaluate his relationship with the patient in terms of the patient's previous interpersonal experiences.

Erich Fromm. Bringing a sociological viewpoint to the field of psychiatric medicine, Fromm believes man must be considered in the light of his cultural environment and the demands of his society, rather than as a purely biological creature. He sees man in constant conflict with nature, limited by the physical fact of his mortality from ever achieving his goals. He places less emphasis on instinct as a motivating force in man and, in general, reduces the importance of biology in comparison to cultural influences. Fromm also gives greater depth to the field of psychotherapy, applying the perspective of the whole of society to the individual member, and extending his theories to a critical study of Western civilization and values.

In addition to the above, later schools have arisen with fundamental concepts that differ from, or are extensive modifications of, the basic Freudian or Freudian-orientated approaches. Foremost among these is the *Chicago School,* the chief spokesmen of which are Franz Alexander and Thomas French. Successful, short-term psychotherapy, as advocated by the Chicago Institute for Psychoanalysis, is one of the main objectives of this school, which for practical reasons rejects the Freudian principle of intensive, long-term psychotherapy. Other contemporary movements include the *London School,* led by Ernest Jones, and the *existential approach,* which denies affiliation with any particular school, but advocates clarification of terms and dogma in the psychiatric field, questioning those that presently exist.

Intensive Individual Psychotherapy. While this is not entirely a "non-Freudian" approach, it is not considered formal analysis. In this therapeutic approach to emotional and mental disorders, patient and psychiatrist face each other, comfortably placed in chairs, and through easy-going discussion or question and answer they probe the patient's unconscious to account for the conscious manifestations of his difficulty, and to determine the reason or reasons for his discomfiture, problem, emotional disturbance, etc. For example, the patient may tell of trouble experienced during his first year in school. He is asked to furnish a reason for this difficulty. His reply, expressed in conscious and socially acceptable explanatory terms, can be dissected as the patient seeks to ascertain the emotional provocation for and inner causes of the scholastic difficulty. If he is unable to provide any answer, the question is temporarily dropped and reinvestigated at a later session when, because of increasing insight, the patient may be ready to reply and to realize the reason for his conflict. Any treatment program which allows a patient to talk freely is using the method known as *ventilation;* it enables him to discharge and bring out in the open all of those life experiences which have been causing him serious concern, either consciously or unconsciously.

Group Therapy. This therapeutic procedure resulted from a shortage of qualified personnel during World War II to care for and treat psychiatric patients. A small group of patients, usually those with neurotic or emotional difficulties, talk about their problems with the therapist serving as moderator. There are many advantages to this form of psychotherapy. In an atmosphere of "misery loves company" the bashful and embarrassed patient is quickly encouraged to "speak up"; he subjectively profits as he objectively and critically surveys, analyzes, and interprets problems in others similar to his own; he learns to yield selfish individualistic impulses to the will of the crowd. He helps and is helped. On the material side is the advantage of more treatment opportunities for more patients at a far lower cost than private therapy. Today group therapy is found not only in institutions and clinics but also in private practice.

ADJUNCTS TO THE PSYCHOLOGICAL APPROACH

In addition to the specific therapeutic programs mentioned above, there are several methods of therapy which may be used to implement the basic treatment program. Of themselves, they would not be sufficient to remove the psychological "root" of the problem, but they can aid the patient in establishing mental and emotional equilibrium. These "adjuncts" are not confined to one school of psychotherapy, but may be used interchangeably as the individual case may require.

Occupational Therapy. This method brings the patient more than a pleasant way to pass the time by weaving, binding books, painting, carving, etc. The patient who is introverted may learn to mingle and work with a group. He discovers that he is not the only one with deep, personal, emotional problems. He becomes empathetic. The patient who is self-deprecatory and lacks confidence in himself finds he can "do something"—he can "make something." New interests are developed; hobbies are discovered. Frequently a patient who has never performed specialized work or has been dissatisfied with his previous occupation, learns and likes a new form of endeavor such as printing, silversmithing, pottery making, stenography, etc.

Hypnosis. Similar to electric shock therapy or tranquilization, hypnosis is *not* a cure. It can dramatically and effectively, for a time at least, remove a symptom, but it does not get at the underlying cause. In a similar manner, the patient who complains of abdominal pain can relieve this distress by an analgesic medication, but until he is thoroughly examined and the actual cause is determined, the basic difficulty will remain. Hypnotism permits the psychiatrist to induce a patient to accept suggestion. This can be done after, as well as during, the hypnotic trance. Suggestion, without hypnosis, is a common feature of any treatment program.

Hypnosis can be synthetic or analytic. The patient can be analyzed under hypnosis as the therapist's questions evoke replies representing unconscious desires, frustrations, and conflicts, without censorship by the conscious mind. Likewise, a synthetic approach may be used, consisting of positive suggestions made while the subject is hypnotized.

Socialization. This term is descriptive of Adolf Meyer's approach to therapy. Every component of the patient's life is studied and assayed. These features include the home and its occupants, relatives, friends, work, religion, interests, economic status—all in addition to the usual case history and the physical, laboratory, and mental examinations. His place in the world and his interpersonal relationships can then be determined. Therapy capitalizes on the individual's assets and treatment aims to eradicate or repair liabilities. This could mean "correcting" the attitude of someone other than the patient—an irascible employer, a teacher who is impatient with an overly shy and sensitive pupil, a carping, fault-finding spouse, etc.

Guidance. In this essentially Adlerian principle, the therapist follows no orthodox protocol in treatment. Instead, he "guides," advises, and suggests, discussing with the patient avenues of thought to be pursued, ideas and habits to be abandoned. It is the nearest parent-child pattern we have in psychotherapy. Its outstanding disadvantage is the increasing dependence the patient feels toward the therapist.

Distributive Analysis and Discharge Catharsis. These two methods of direct contact in therapy were propounded by Oskar Diethelm. The former is a question and answer procedure. The latter is a procedure wherein the patient speaks freely, without interruption, on any subject he chooses—he "cleanses" his mind of an emotional burden. These two methods are largely the *modi operandi* of intensive individual psychotherapy.

Psychodrama. Created by Dr. J. L. Moreno, psychodrama uses the stage as a medium in which patients, singly or in groups, "act" out their problems. It is alleged that both as performer and spectator, the patient develops insight into his emotional difficulty.

Persuasion. Originally championed by Dubois, this is a self-explanatory term. Persuasion is particularly useful in the treatment of children.

Suggestion. Written of enthusiastically by Hippocrates, this method was popularized by Bernheim in the latter part of the nineteenth century. It is a readily understandable approach, akin to persuasion, and it is used by all of us in our everyday interpersonal activity.

Recreation Therapy. This therapeutic adjunct is more than entertainment. It dates back to Celsus and Pinel and their belief in "intellectual diversion." Recreation is applicable to the individual (fishing, hunting, stamp collecting), as well as to the group (dances, athletics, attendance at motion pictures, etc.). Like occupational therapy, it fosters "group" activity, develops healthy, interpersonal relationships, teaches, and enables the patient "to do"; it is an outlet for aggression and hostility, it can develop new interests and, of course, it presents diversion and entertainment. Prominent in this field is music therapy, which may range from choral groups, orchestras, and individual instrumental instruction to appreciation of music.

Desensitization. This is the procedure wherein the patient is required to face the traumatic and unpleasant experiences of his past. It is brought about by having the patient discuss, at frequently repeated interviews, the conflict material elicited originally through ventilation. These interviews are repeated until the patient can review his experiences without excessive emotional concern. Normal emotional reaction is to be expected, however, and it is neither desirable nor necessary to expect a complete loss of emotional reaction in connection with those events that should normally cause concern. It is the *excess* of concern that is pathological and requires alleviation. The term "desensitization" is also applied to the procedure carried out in assuaging fear or other symptom manifestations in definite situations. Here the patient is required to face the problem repeatedly until he no longer presents the symptoms in that situation, or until he is able to tolerate or ignore the symptoms if they occur. It is necessary, of course, to encourage and reassure these patients frequently while this procedure is executed. With such therapy, for example, a young girl who fainted every time she saw or heard of blood was able to overcome this tendency completely. Desensitization is especially valuable in the symptomatic treatment of fear reactions.

Re-education. This is carried out in connection with all of the previously mentioned disciplines. It is essentially the development of clear insight on the part of the patient into the mechanism of his illness, the establishment of new habits of response (as in desensitization), and the formulation by him of an adequate occupational, social, and recreational program to ensure future stabilization. It is often advisable to desensitize the patient's family to his illness and re-educate them into new habits of response toward him.

LAY COUNSELING AND THERAPY

A confused public wants to and should know where lay counseling and treatment fit in the therapeutic picture, if at all, and not only if these modalities are helpful but whether they are harmful. If a discussion of this burning issue by a certified psychiatrist is prejudiced by the high ethics of the medical profession then we have no defense, but we do present what we honestly and wholeheartedly believe to be an unbiased estimation.

Counselors. The psychiatrist is *not* a counselor; he is a *therapist*. Since he is not a deity he cannot decide for the patient what is right or wrong. Treatment, as it progresses, should bring the patient insight which enables him to make such decisions for himself. Whenever a patient asks a question such as, "Am I right?" or "What's wrong with that?" such queries are *prima facie* evidence of troublesome, unconscious feelings of guilt and doubt.

By the same token, a counselor is not a psychiatrist. Treatment is and should be at the hands of the physician. If the individual seeks only advice he can consult a counselor—or an attorney.

Lay Therapy. For the past few years this subject has been a bone of contention between psychiatrists and psychologists. A "cooling-off" truce is currently maintained between the American Psychiatric Association and the American Psychological Association, but with little hope of a mutual agreement in sight. In addition to psychologists clamoring for the unrestricted right to practice psychotherapy, there are social workers who seek parallel privileges. Much is made, by nonmedical practitioners, of Sigmund Freud's original sanction of lay analysts, in which he was vigorously opposed by colleagues such as Jones and Brill. Freud had a valid reason for his action. He was anxious to spread his "gospel" and gain recognition at a time when the medical profession was loath to acknowledge psychoanalysis as a legitimate modality of medical practice. Consequently, Freud was willing to have others practice analysis, if only to popularize it.

Why should a therapist and/or an analyst be a medical man first and then a specialized psychiatrist? We are learning, as time and research progress, that the psyche (mind) can no longer be regarded as an isolated item of a human being; it is too intimately linked with the soma (body). Other than purely psychological features are irrevocably involved. They include chemical, biological, physiological, anatomical, and metabolic aspects. Therefore, the therapist must be oriented and fully grounded in all phases of medicine before he attempts treatment of an emotional and/or a mental illness. Tests, examinations, consultations, and prescriptions may be needed during treatment.

To these protests the lay practitioner retorts that he will not treat a patient without first securing "medical clearance" by a doctor. But what of clinical features that may arise during therapy which only a physician can recognize? For instance, a patient complaining of nothing other than depression may be found "normal" in his physical examination. Let us assume he commences psychotherapy. A few weeks later he complains of vague headaches and occasional nausea. The nonmedical practitioner, initially assured that there is no organic pathology present in the patient, would feel justified in regarding these symptoms as purely psychogenic in origin. However, a prompt neurological examination may reveal evidence of a brain tumor in the "silent" (without outward clinical indications) area of the temporal lobe! Immediate surgery will probably be lifesaving and totally cure the so-called depression. If the patient's condition were allowed to progress to the point of projectile vomiting—a late sign of brain tumor—surgery would probably be futile. Again, a patient may complain of increasing fatigue, listlessness, and indifference. These could easily be psychological features. Nevertheless, an examination of a blood specimen for "blood-protein-bound iodine" (the modern successor to basal metabolism determination) may well reveal an insufficiently functioning thyroid gland which, in the average physical examination, may fail to present the dire indications of a severely hypofunctioning thyroid.

Finally, it is not uncommon for a psychiatrist to prescribe hormones, ataractics, etc., for a patient while he undergoes treatment. Such modalities often require change, replacement, etc., as the physician may deem advisable from clinical evidence and constant examination. Such a patient may fail to receive this necessary adjuvant therapy if he is treated by a lay practitioner. Or, if the latter plans to have a medical man conduct this part of treatment, the patient cannot possibly have full confidence in the lay therapist and total transference is lacking. In addition, there is the needless expense of paying two men when one can and should do.

INSTITUTIONALIZATION

Contemporary treatment and the latest advances have cast their beneficial shadows on institutions, public and private. The changes are best described in an editorial in the *Journal of the American Psychiatric Association,* as follows:

"Advances in medical science may be amazing from time to time, but let these not be confined only to reports from laboratory, operating room or general hospital wards. Contemplation of clinical psychiatry furnishes food for thought and satisfaction to the therapeutically minded. In the last 15 years the great increase in the number of young psychiatrists and the rapid improvement in the quality of their training is showing significant impact on treatment procedures for patients. Some observers of the clinical scene are ready to agree that therapeutic skill in psychotherapy is now far more specific than in any dictionary definition of the term, and is peculiarly effective either with or without those ever satisfying aids in the management of patients known as somatic therapies. Whatever the degree of this may be, it does point the finger at sharp acceleration in the changing role of hospitals, both general and psychiatric, in their reception and treatment of psychiatric patients.

"Thirty or more years ago the psychiatric patient was brought to the hospital by the family just about as often as he was sent by a referring physician. Contacts with a psychiatrist as a consultant were occasional, but rarely did the psychiatrist follow the patient into the hospital since, in most instances, psychiatric hospitals furnished full-time medical, psychiatric, and nursing care. Hospitals were not too closely related to community life, involved the family very little in the treatment situation, and rarely had much contact with the family doctor. After the patient had been studied and given treatment in every way possible, when the time came to leave, the patient was literally handed out the door, disappeared into his home or his work with no follow-up by the hospital nor any particular contact with what medical care or program would be available henceforth. In other words, there was no integration with the background or family personal setting that may have contributed to the formation of the illness, nor was there planful, progressive reorganization of the post-hospital period except by those interested in the patient, including the family doctor, who may have had little or no contact with the program carried on in the hospital. Today, however, psychiatric hospitals are beginning to establish a different procedure. In some instances the majority of patients admitted are seen as regularly by their referring physicians as they are by the full-time hospital staff. The consulting psychiatrist, or the doctor, leads the patient by the hand to the hospital, continues his relationship with the patient during the hospital treatment, and is involved in it. When the hospital period is completed the doctor leads his patient back home to work and family and a continued therapeutic program based on what is fundamental in psychotherapy.

"This procedure illustrates what is termed 'the longitudinal pattern in psychiatric therapy,' which should be considered a new important theme in psychiatric medicine." *

PROGNOSIS

The prospect for success in treatment of mental illness could be didactically expressed in a table based on irrefutable statistics, but this would be a rigid, circumscribed presentation. In all frankness, the prognosis must be eclectic in outlook. In other words, therapeutic results in two patients manifesting identical signs and symptoms may mean complete recovery for one and not the other.

Fifty years ago a "recovered" case of schizophrenia was unheard of; today it is not surprising for a mental hospital to report recovery in 40 per cent of the cases. Since 1958, of all the patients admitted to mental institutions, more than half were released within the same year. More and more epileptics, with

* Editorial, *Journal of the American Psychiatric Association*, October, 1958.

secure pharmaceutical control of their seizures, are driving vehicles and taking their places in industry. Antibiotics are enabling mongoloid children to survive infections of infancy, to grow, and to be trained. Formerly unapproachable, withdrawn, and diffident mentally retarded persons are enjoying personality reversals thanks to hormonal therapy, and they are becoming amenable to instruction. Slowly but surely, the problems of alcoholism and drug addiction are being shifted from the hands of penologists to those of psychiatrists, and both state and Federal institutions are undergoing changes to conform to this newer concept. Less and less judicial intervention is required as developments in therapy and the promise of relief induce patients to seek hospital treatment on a voluntary basis. Finally, the introduction of ataractics has made possible the welcome "open-door" policy, which is in a sense analogous to that great period at the end of the eighteenth century when Pinel struck the chains from the mentally ill at the "insane asylum" at the Salpêtrière. Now the bolts and bars are being "struck" from the mental hospitals.

As the author stressed in the Foreword, this book is not intended as a "do-it-yourself" handbook for amateur psychiatry. A psychiatric case is a medical case and the emotionally disturbed individual can do as much harm trying to treat himself as he could in trying to treat his own malignant tumor. Naturally one is driven to ask, "What are the chances of recovery or improvement in a given case?" Results cannot be measured in statistics or based on blind faith in textbook predictions, but are dependent upon the individual's potentiality for accepting therapy for his psychic handicap and upon his finding the "best" therapist. This is the physician in whom the patient has unqualified confidence. Finally, it should always be remembered that each person as an individual has fears, conflicts, tensions, and anxieties different from any other, although the symptoms in both may be identical. Herein lies the major challenge of psychiatry.

Outside the scope of the clinical laboratory are certain personality disorders, evinced as sociopathologic behavior. These have been described as "disorders of psychogenic origin without clearly defined tangible cause or structural change." This group of disorders has long been, and continues to be, a thorn in psychiatry's side, owing to the wraith-like elusiveness of cause, diagnosis, and treatment. Why is anyone a misfit? What creates a delinquent? Why is there sexual deviation?

CHARACTERISTICS OF THE DISORDERED PERSONALITY

Over a period of two decades this category of mental illness has undergone several changes—a self-evident indication of the uncertainty enveloping this type of disorder. Descriptive labels have ranged from "constitutional psychopathic inferiority," "psychopathic personality," and others, to the informal term familiarly used by psychiatrists, "psychopath." The hedging adjective "constitutional" at once reveals a lack of knowledge as to whether these individuals are born with aberrant reaction patterns or develop them during life. At a military court-martial the case of a "psychopath" was summarized as follows: *He is what he is because he always has been what he is, and he will always be what he is.*

The psychopathic personality is characterized by emotional disequilibrium and gross errors in judgment. Such a person is the quintessence of egocentricity; he is disdainful of the sentimental, scoffs at the Golden Rule, sneers at patriotism, and has a firm negative reply to the query, "Am I my brother's keeper?" He is deaf to plea, unheeding of lecture, and cannot profit from precept. He subscribes to the tenet, "Here today, gone tomorrow," and believes "the world owes me a living." To quote one penologist, "He would kill his own mother if the murder meant a buck." Fundamentally this individual is a paranoid, and he struts through life, rudely elbowing aside all rules of fair play. Yet, when opposition is too powerful for him to overcome, the psychopath becomes the sniveling, quaking, cringing person who begs for mercy or special consideration. All this we know, but why some people behave in this fashion and others do not, *we simply do not know.*

Many psychopaths are materially successful, even recipients of public respect. The psychopathic high-pressure salesman whose commissions during prosperous times run into astronomical figures may spend his money liberally and indiscriminately. He is the devotee of bistros and race tracks, the darling of chorines and widows, the patron saint of maîtres-d'hôtel. Yet, when Dame Fortune turns her back on him, he is the first to line up at unemployment benefit windows, to approach friends for assistance, and, above all, to wail in self-pity about his "hard luck" or about how "the cards are stacked against him." All of us have experienced self-pity at some time in life but the normal individual is able to control it. Of this emotional reaction, peculiar to man, Archibald Rutledge writes in *Santee Paradise:* "In nature we do not discover despondency, the handmaid of despair; we never find self-pity, which undermines virtue more subtly than arrant vice, yet as effectively. Wild things do not resign or surrender; they will fight to the death. Even a butterfly will defend itself. All living things love life, and if we do not love it enough to make it seem worth while to ourselves and others, a natural suspicion arises that there must be something the matter with us. Take self-pity out of life and you would be making great progress in the redemption of humanity. It is really a disease and, I take it, a disease incident to civilization, for as we go back toward nature we find less of it and in nature's home none at all. Her children are valiant. Whatever may be their adversities, they do not complain; they are self-reliant, and they never lose hope." *

The so-called "successful" type of psychopathic personality has produced many alluring figures, such as Wilson Mizner, Bet-a-

---

* Archibald Rutledge, *Santee Paradise* (New York: The Bobbs-Merrill Co., Inc., 1956) , p. 230. Used by special permission of the publishers.

Million Gates, Diamond Jim Brady, Steve Brodie, and François Villon, but it is highly doubtful that these men were paragons of mental and emotional adjustment.

There are many varieties of personality disorders and associated psychopathic states, the principal of which will be discussed below. These include the emotionally unstable personality, the compulsive personality, homosexuality, and other pathologic sexual deviations.

THE EMOTIONALLY UNSTABLE PERSONALITY

The emotionally unstable individual reacts with excitability and ineffectiveness under minor stress, with the result that his judgment is undependable. His relationship to other people is continuously fraught with fluctuating emotional attitudes, owing to strong and poorly controlled hostility, guilt, and anxiety. Several prominent types deserve mention.

The Passive-Aggressive Personality. Reactions in this group are of three varieties, but all are manifestations of the same underlying psychopathology and frequently they are seen to occur interchangeably in the same individual. In these cases, the clinical picture usually has superimposed upon it an anxiety reaction which is typically psychoneurotic.

The *passive-dependent type* is characterized by helplessness, indecisiveness, and a tendency to cling to others as a dependent child to a supporting parent. Such a person is recognized under the popular term "clinging vine."

The *passive-aggressive type* reacts to life situations with passive measures that have an aggressive tinge, such as pouting, stubbornness, procrastination, inefficiency, and obstructionism. Typical of this group is the chronic objector to progressive change.

The *aggressive type* reacts to frustration with irritability, temper tantrums, and destructive behavior as dominant manifestations. A specific characteristic of this reaction is a morbid or pathological resentment. A deep dependency is usually evident in such cases.

The Compulsive Personality. Individuals in this subgroup are characterized by chronic, excessive, or obsessive concern with adherence to standards of conscience or conformity. They may be overinhibited, overconscientious, and may have an inordinate capacity for work. Typically they are rigid and lack a normal ability to relax. While their chronic tension may lead to neurotic illness, this is not an invariable consequence. The reaction may appear as a persistence of an adolescent pattern of behavior or as a regression from more mature functioning as a result of stress.

HOMOSEXUALITY

The popular conception of the homosexual, not surprisingly, revolves about the extreme example: the cosmetized, effeminate man who seeks male companionship for amorous purposes, and his female counterpart, the so-called "lesbian"—a gruff, swaggering, aggressive, masculine female who seeks out other women with the same intentions. These persons actually represent only a minority of homosexuals. By recalling the principle expressed in Chapter 2, that of recognizing the gradation of differences among individuals, the reader can appreciate that most homosexuals cannot be identified as such. Mannerisms, dress, facial expressions, and vocal pitch are poor indicators. The first homosexual this writer ever encountered clinically was a tall, muscular, hard-hitting halfback who won honorable mention as an All-American gridiron selection! But here again we are confining ourselves to the extreme phase of homosexuality. Let us take the larger view.

From what source is the word "homosexual" derived? *Homo* in Latin means "man"; however, although zoological derivatives refer to the species of mammals, including mankind, they also refer to the primates (hence, *homo sapiens,* the wise or intelligent branch of the species). A more likely basis for the word "homosexual" is the Greek *homo,* which means "the same" or "of like kind." In the most general sense, then, a group of students in a dormitory, a "gang" of youths, soldiers in barracks, even a ladies' sewing circle, would have to be acknowledged as a "homosexual" conglomerate. And indeed it is in some of these areas of strong unisexual concentration that deviations are most noticeable. But this is not evidence of higher incidence, for homosexuals are known to come from all walks of life: business, industry, the professions, unskilled labor, etc.

Another misconception is that nearly all "practicing" homosexuals travel in "bands" and live quite apart from the community at large, without stability, without homes and families. To the contrary, psychiatrists and psychological counselors encounter many men and women who indulge in homosexual activities although they are married, raising children, serving in P.T.A.'s and holding down responsible jobs.

It has been said that it is the rare person who can be completely masculine or completely feminine, as befits his or her biological lot, since everyone is endowed with characteristics derived from chromosomes handed down by both male and female ancestors (Jung's concept of the *Anlage*). This biological process permits a man to appreciate the beauty of fine fabrics and the refinements of grace in posture and movement; it also makes it possible for the young girl to enjoy camping and woodcraft and to play vigorous tennis; it enables the mature woman to seek a career in business or to become a crusader (Carrie Nation, for example). As a matter of pride and in response to pressure from our cultural milieu, however, most men and women tend to conceal the characteristics they have which are representative of the opposite sex.

The commonest spur to homosexuality seems to be alcoholism. Many of the actions of the drunkard are veiled homosexual gestures—the familiar slap on the buttocks, the fraternal embrace, etc. Until recent times the pub and the saloon were centers of male gatherings and these locales became ideal breeding places for unisexual associations. Present-day counterparts are drinking centers known as "gay bars," not hard to find in the larger cities and usually identified by signs reading "The Red Tiger," "The Blue Cat," etc. Alcohol, as a depressant of inhibitory centers, makes possible the overt release of divertive sexual drives which are unacceptable to most of our society. When an emotional conflict arises from strife between unconscious homosexual drives and superego taboos, intoxication succeeds in blotting out the latter and the road is clear for homosexual gratification.

What causes homosexuality in its more extreme forms? Sigmund Freud postulated five responsible factors: (1) overattachment to the mother; (2) overevaluation of the phallus; (3) fear of the father; (4) jealousy toward an older sibling (brother or sister); and (5) early homosexual seduction. The mother who overstresses the importance of the genital organs or erogenous zones (through prolonged, vigorous washing in bathing the child, for example) may teach the youngster to derive pleasure from stimulation of that area. Parental harping on the evils and dire consequences of masturbation may arouse in the child greater curiosity than if the subject had been reduced to its proper minor importance.

Unfortunately, however, only the deepest kind of probing succeeds in eliciting background information, from either the homosexual or his family, that would assist the therapist. In despair and resignation, we accept the common concept "he is what he is" and as a result, psychiatric literature is replete with clinical reports to the effect that "the homosexual is born that way" and "seldom if ever can a homosexual be converted to a heterosexual."

It is worth noting, on the subject of homosexuality, that there are individuals superficially adjusted to their heterosexual role in society, even to the extent of having large families of their own, who concurrently indulge in homosexual practices. A prominent example of this "ambisexual" type was Oscar Wilde, but such persons are not uncommon in our communities.

OTHER FORMS OF SEXUAL DEVIATION

It is extremely difficult to establish a fine line of distinction between "normal" and "abnormal" sexual behavior. The Kinsey report is only one of many sources that has pointed out that well-adjusted, happily married couples experiment with and occasionally resort to "perverted" physiological activity. Again it is a matter of degree: the person who constantly and exclusively indulges in sexual perversions can be justifiably regarded as not normal in his genital life. Generally, though, such a person shows other evidences of abnormality in behavior: alcoholism, narcotism, criminality, or rebellion against customs and mores of the environment and the times.

Only brief mention will be made of the commoner forms of sexual perversion. Abundant treatment of the subject is to be found in the works of Krafft-Ebing, Havelock Ellis, George W. Henry, and Alfred Kinsey.

Voyeurism. This is the quest for sexual gratification by surreptitiously watching someone who is undressed or undressing, or persons who are cohabiting. The voyeur is popularly referred to as a "peeping Tom," in allusion to the quasi-legendary tale of Lady Godiva. The entertainment industry derives part of its success from the vicarious stimulation it provides voyeurs, especially burlesque show habitués and those who frequent other "girlie" spectacles.

Fetishism. In fetishism, an inanimate object is personalized as a love object (a stocking, a glove, a shoe, etc.). In one variation, any bodily maneuver or nongenital part of the body may be the source of erotic stimulation.

Flagellation. Whipping (prompted by sadism) and allowing oneself to be whipped (prompted by masochism) have been known to furnish the stimulus for sexual excitement.

Fellatio and Cunnilingus. Oral manipulation of the genital organ stimulates sexual arousal. In the case of the male organ it is known as fellatio, of the female genitalia, cunnilingus.

Pederasty. Sexual intercourse per rectum (usually with a boy) is referred to as pederasty; a synonym is *buggery,* or *sodomy* (not necessarily with a boy). Related to this is *bestiality,* intercourse with lower animals.

Exposure. Perhaps the mildest form of sexual perversion is exposure. It is commonly found in clinical cases of old men who have revealed their genitalia to young girls. Invariably senile confusion underlies the practice, with sexual wishful thinking involved.

Not every sexual pervert is a psychopath, for perversion is not unknown in neurotics and psychotics. Again, the unusual in genital activity may be prompted by circumstances which the French call *faute de mieux*—for example, men aboard ship for weeks at a time, unisexual schools, and prisons.

SOCIOPATHY

Within this category "illness" is regarded in terms of an abnormal attitude toward society; it implies inability or unwillingness to conform to the prevailing cultural milieu. Sociopathic reactions are often symptomatic, indicating severe underlying personality disorder, neurosis, or psychosis; or they may occur as a result of organic brain injury or disease. There are two main subtypes: antisocial and dyssocial reaction.

Antisocial Reaction. This term refers to the chronically antisocial person who is "always in trouble," profiting neither from experience nor punishment and maintaining no genuine loyalties to any person, group, or code. He is frequently callous and hedonistic, showing marked emotional immaturity, and lacking a sense of responsibility. His judgment is poor, and he often attempts to rationalize his behavior so that it appears warranted, reasonable, and justified. In this group we find the hobo, the draft dodger, the radical, etc.

Dyssocial Reaction. The dyssocial individual is a psychopath with "asocial and amoral trends." This person manifests disregard for the usual social codes and is repeatedly coming into conflict with them. The criminal and the delinquent are often included in this group. However, not every criminal and delinquent is necessarily a psychopath. The same background factors (broken home, unstable parents, catastrophic childhood frustrations, and intense hostility against authority) that provide a setting for dyssocial reaction can also produce a neurotic or psychotic reaction whose dominant expression will be in terms of crime. In this regard, one tends to think at once of *juvenile* delinquency, and the thought is not amiss. Approximately *one fourth* of all arrests in this country are of persons twenty-one years of age or younger. Crime is increasing a bit more rapidly than population, but adolescent offenders are soaring in numbers eight times faster than adults. Scientific and popular literature are filled with articles on the alleged "cause" or "causes" of this mounting juvenile delinquency: television, radio, motion pictures, and comic books, with their "attractive" presentations of crime; disintegration of old-fashioned, wholesome family life; lowering of moral standards; lax disciplinary measures; indifference to religion; and the extremes of progressive education.

Over the past few years psychiatry has stepped into the picture. More and more delinquent children are being remanded to psychiatric rather than correctional institutions. In New York State no penal institution is without full-time psychiatric service. Within communities the rising tide of juvenile delinquency could be slowed down, if not indeed stemmed, by increased support for police athletic leagues, church-sponsored clubs, school and civic centers, after-class organized activities, and supervised playgrounds.

The person who is unwilling or unable to cope with his problems has several possible avenues of escape. Not all of these have tragic consequences; many individuals who have dreamed of luxuries and adventure have been willing to settle for a safe, humdrum existence. Others, beset by the turmoil of strong libidinal impulses, experience such a sense of disappointment and frustration in their unsuccessful struggle to attain maturity that they take refuge in a neurosis, they may create their own world (schizophrenia), or they may seek satisfaction in delinquent behavior. Some individuals who are unable to face their problems, however, permit themselves to become addicted to intoxicants or narcotics, which temporarily blot out from their consciousness the unpleasant aspects of whatever may be troubling them. All these reaction patterns serve the same purpose—the casting off of responsibility. All of them are distinctly infantile mechanisms.

GASTROINTESTINAL ORIENTATION

The reader will recall from the discussion in Chapter 1 how an individual's emotional life in infancy is centered around his gastrointestinal tract, and how infantile attachments tend to persist in adulthood as problem-saving devices. All addictions involve oral or parenteral consumption of some substance, liquid or solid, which provides a transitory relief by producing exhilaration, release from inhibition, or a sojourn in a fantasy world. The addict has indeed reverted to his babyhood, wherein all his wants were satisfied orally—even in the case of the drug addict who takes his narcotic hypodermically, it is often found that he began with marijuana-loaded cigarettes.

The range of addiction is very great, reaching all the way from the plight of the Skid Row drunk and the "hophead" to the equally abject if less dramatic situation of the compulsive devourer of patent medicines, candy bars, cigarettes, and midnight snacks. For what is addiction? So often do we associate the word exclusively with the use of alcohol and narcotics that the full compass of its meaning escapes us. Anyone who is habituated, inclined, or prone to some pattern in a compulsive fashion is, in truth, "addicted." And while it is, admittedly, the chronic alcoholic and the "user" who present the more serious social problem, on a psychological basis there is fundamentally little difference between the drives of these people and those of chain-smokers, compulsive "nibblers," and gourmands.

PERSONALITY FACTORS

Why does one person become an addict and not another? There is a common tendency to place the blame on external circumstances ("she started drinking after her husband died," or, "he fell in with the wrong crowd and began taking dope"). Clinical experience does not support this situational type of interpretation. A characteristic preaddiction mixture of unfavorable personality factors is encountered in all addicts: weakness of will, a feeble superego coupled with a poorly integrated ego, incapacity to live in a competitive world, and inability to face disappointments and frustrations. These pieces make up the personality mosaic of the addicted individual, whether his addiction is to alcohol, narcotics, cigarettes, medicine, or food.

Addicted or habituated persons display still another common emotional reaction, defeatism, which is reflected not only in their general outlook but also in their attitude toward their addiction. Consider the obese wife who bewails her excessive weight, in the full realization that she has risked losing her husband's affections. She resolves to follow a strict diet, and indeed she becomes a very talented calculator of calories. But after each calorie-poor meal she lies down to read a novel, while she pops one bonbon after another into her mouth. When reproached for her lack of fortitude she moans, like the alcoholic and the drug addict, "I just can't help it. I have no resistance." This, too, is the excuse of the four-packs-a-day smoker whose cardiologist has issued warning after warning.

All addicts are sisters (or brothers) under the skin—*their psychosexual development has been faulty.* Somewhere along the road of chronological advancement their acceleration toward maturity has not kept pace with their years. Most often their growth has been arrested—the libido is "fixed"—at the narcissistic level and they must *ingest* something to assuage their feelings of anxiety. Instead of facing up to antagonistic forces outside themselves, such individuals incorporate into their own bodies something which will help them to "live through" the situation privately, without assuming the responsibility that is required in interpersonal relations. Such a pattern of reaction is almost indistinguishable from that employed by the infant.

It is likely that the arrest in psychosexual development occurs rather early in the life of these individuals, since some persons reared in strife-torn or broken homes, or in a climate of either excessively strict or lax discipline, manage to solve their problems satisfactorily and reach adulthood in an excellent state of adjustment. Others become resentful of authority quite early and despise social dictates; these are the ones who, admitting defeat in the struggle to climb the ladder of psychosexual development to emotional maturity, habitually seek the "missing thrill."

ALCOHOLISM

From time immemorial man has been coping with the problem of intoxication. Probably not long after the stimulating qualities of certain herbs were discovered, their habitual use developed, and soon the technique of fermentation was mastered. In all latitudes and longitudes men have found ways to extract stimulating substances from grain, potatoes, rice, corn, cactus, sugar, and countless other resources. Only a few cultures (notably the Jewish and the Mohammedan) have escaped from the destructive effects of intoxicants. Whole nations have been ruined, armies betrayed, and great undertakings placed in jeopardy despite religious preachings and governmental restrictions. It cannot be said with assurance that any one racial or national group is more given to the use of intoxicants than another. An edict issued in Paris against the sale of absinthe contained the observation that the world's highest alcoholic consumption is in France. The habitual use of intoxicants is common among the Irish, and drunkenness has become a serious problem in Soviet Russia, where one would expect the state to be strategically empowered to control behavior. In the United States the public health problem of alcoholism is surpassed only by that of heart disease, cancer, and mental disorders.

Paradoxes of Alcohol. In its natural state or in beverage form, alcohol is an endless paradox. Of itself it cannot be detected on the breath; the odor that one smells is always the flavoring added to make it potable. Of all foodstuffs alcohol is the easiest to digest, and it is totally digestible. In moderate doses it is medically useful (to the noncompulsive drinker) in a number of ways: to provide relaxation, to relieve the pain of rheumatoid arthritis, to stimulate the appetite, aid digestion, and assist in alleviating the symptoms of the common cold. Although alcohol is the *bête noire* of the highway (only 0.04 per cent alcohol in the blood may reduce visual acuity as much as the wearing of dark glasses after sundown), a group of beer-swilling volunteers at the Yale Center of Alcoholic Studies actually *outperformed* their abstinent competitors in a series of special machine-efficiency tests. A "drinker" is not necessarily an "alcoholic," and many steady drinkers could not become alcoholics no matter how hard they tried. One New York physician, determined to test this statement, loaded his station wagon with two cases of liquor and drove to a lonely cabin in New England. Alone and totally out of contact with the world, he drank and sang day after day, night after night. "But," as Milton Golin reported in the July 19, 1958, *Journal of the American Medical Association,* "he was not happy. At the end of one solid month of inebriation, when this doctor returned to his office to measure his craving and physical dependency on alcohol as a drug, only one thing was certain—*he did not want to look at liquor for the rest of his life.*"

As a final paradox, while alcohol is commonly referred to as a "stimulant" it is actually a depressant. By depressing inhibitory centers in the brain, it allows the individual unhampered expression of underlying drives, released in what appears to be a state of stimulation. A single drink may suffice to convert the timid, apprehensive speaker into a self-confident orator; his timidity has been "depressed" and his yearning for the approval of his audience has been freed for expression.

What Is Alcoholism? How are we to define "alcoholism"? Numerous investigators have pointed out that the habitual use of intoxicants cannot be ascribed to the mere availability of alcoholic beverages. Milton Golin stated that "alcoholism is basically a brain disease—insofar as the brain is (1) a physiological organ subject to mental and emotional stresses and (2) a sociological organ subject to interpersonal demands and byplay." Mark Keller, managing editor of the *Quarterly Journal of Alcohol Studies,* regards alcoholism as "a chronic behavioral disorder manifested by repeated drinking of alcoholic beverages in excess of the dietary social usages of the community and to the extent that it interferes with the individual's health or his social or economic functioning." WHO (World Health Organization) puts it succinctly: "One becomes an alcoholic when he begins to be concerned about how activities interfere with his drinking instead of how drinking interferes with his activities." An ancient oriental proverb describes the downward progression of alcoholism very well:

> "First the man takes a drink,
> Then the drink takes a drink,
> Then the drink takes a man."

Alcoholism is not a disease *per se.* Rather it is a symptom of a complex and all-inclusive pathological situation which involves the individual's mind, body, morals, and spiritual existence—not to mention his environmental and interpersonal relationships. That alcohol attacks many parts of the body is a clinical fact. When taken in excessive quantities it may produce gastric and duodenal ulcers, injure brain and nerve tissue, generate cirrhosis (hardening) of the liver, and lay the groundwork for nephritis (inflammation of the kidney). The occurrence of one or another, or several of these conditions in a given individual is generally unpredictable. However, alcohol *always* affects the psyche, wreaking havoc with the emotional structure of the drinker. Alcoholism is found to be part of the pattern of so wide a range of clinical diagnostic entities that it is coming to be regarded as a problem chiefly within the jurisdiction of the psychiatrist.

Fitting alcoholism into the framework of mental illnesses has long been a perplexing problem. For many years the difficulty was peremptorily solved with the term "psychosis with alcoholism"—a meaningless bit of hedging. It would be hard to say how many persons so diagnosed over the years were more eligible for categorization under manic-depressive psychosis, schizophrenia, or some other diagnostic group. The most recent revision of the American Psychiatric Association's classification places alcoholism under "personality disorders," in recognition of the current concept that the habitual use of intoxicants bespeaks a basic personality flaw—a desire for flight into addiction. We noted that in the beginning it is *the man who takes the drink,* then the *drink which takes a drink.* At this juncture it is exclusively a personality disorder. In the tragic stage of alcoholism (when *the drink takes the man*), one sees the more clearly cut and progressively destructive picture of the diagnostic entities which characterize the illness. In this later stage the individual's personality, his behavior, and his organ systems undergo increasing destruction.

The Varieties of Alcoholism. The classical variations of alcoholism are: pathological intoxication, chronic intoxication, alcoholic paranoid states, delirium tremens, acute hallucinosis, and Korsakoff's reaction.

PATHOLOGICAL INTOXICATION. The individual found in a state of pathological intoxication invariably is one who has shown abnormal personality traits prior to his intoxication and who continues to manifest them between bouts with alcohol. In much the same way as the epileptic, he frequently presents antithetic traits. He may harbor an introverted, asocial, schizoid personality.

Pathological intoxication differs from the common garden variety of drunkenness qualitatively rather than quantitatively. True, the "nonpathological" drunk and the pathologic one may both give vent to loud, even violent, behavior. But the latter's excitement takes place in the midst of a dazed state accompanied by excessive emotional display, usually of anxiety or rage, which sometimes attains the height of blazing fury and blind choler. Auditory hallucinations are not uncommon. Although the attack ordinarily lasts but a few minutes, it may persist for hours. Automatic violent behavior may be carried out, even homicidal assault, but the individual recalls nothing of this deportment during the attack when he "comes out of it." Upon being confronted with an account of his actions, he is tearfully remorseful.

CHRONIC INTOXICATION. An alternative term for this condition is "alcoholic deterioration." This is the Skid Row bum—physically, morally, mentally, sociologically, and spiritually at the very nadir of human existence. His chief dread is society, but not far behind is his abhorrence of nourishment. Along his downhill road to this sad state the "chronic alcoholic" can be easily recognized by his refusal to eat. First he begins to miss meals that will interrupt his libations; then he cuts his diet to intermittent snacks; finally, he refuses all solid foods and any beverages that lack alcohol. It is the person in this state—undernourished and in a general condition of dilapidation—who encourages the common notion that alcohol is the guilty factor, whereas it has been only an accomplice in this self-destructive effort. Indeed, there are investigators who interpret the tendency to destroy the self as a latent force in the personality, and who point to habitual, compulsive use of alcohol as an expression of the will to die (a type of psychological suicide).

ALCOHOLIC PARANOID STATES. The person who tries to "blot out" life with alcoholic beverages is fundamentally paranoid. When this personality feature is predominantly outstanding in the clinical picture, the diagnostic term used is "alcoholic paranoid state." Here are the confirmed drinkers who are suspicious, distrustful, sullen, irritable, argumentative, and who may have delusions, chiefly persecutory in nature. The world has "given them a dirty deal"; no one will "give them a break." It is this type of alcoholic who best substantiates the Freudian theory that latent homosexuality finds its compromise in drinking. Out of this complex of drives and frustrations, the paranoid alcoholic develops intense, though often subtle, homosexual relationships with his companions at bars and "clubs." Incidents of brutality following alcoholic debauches at saloons frequently are precipitated by rivalries that grow out of these relationships.

DELIRIUM TREMENS. Known commonly as "d.t.'s," this is the most dangerous of all acute and periodic manifestations of chronic alcohol addiction. Usually preceded by a prolonged bout during which the patient has not eaten, delirium tremens is recognized as the denouement of an alcoholic deterioration. The classical symptoms have been explained in literature as visual hallucinations in the form of "pink elephants," "green snakes," and the like, which the victim feels are pursuing him. He is fearful at the sight of these weird spectacles but in his delirious state presents a "grim humor" in reaction to his helpless plight. In delirium, the patient's sensorium is clouded. He is confused, disoriented, and out of contact with his environment, although he may be induced to respond from time to time. He is highly suggestible (the visual hallucinations can be induced by mere suggestion). Not infrequently his behavior in response to delusions will mimic the features of his occupation; thus, the mail carrier may "make his rounds," walking back and forth in his room and placing imaginary letters in imaginary boxes.

The alarming facet of delirium tremens is its physical component. There is marked prostration, a weak, rapid pulse (itself an indication of a serious outlook), and a cold, clammy skin with profuse perspiration. Obvious symptoms are violent tremors during the acute phase which lasts from three to six days. Should the victim survive this onslaught, he sinks into a deep sleep and awakens comparatively clear mentally but very weak physically. Often the medical measures have to be heroic in an effort to preserve the patient's life. The heart must be watched closely, alkalies and fluids must be administered intravenously, and spinal drainage may be necessary.

Acute Hallucinosis. In some instances, following a spree of intense drinking, there may be a brief period in which the individual experiences frightening auditory hallucinations. The condition, called "acute hallucinosis," may last from a few hours to one or two days. The patient reacts to his hallucinations with abject fear.

Korsakoff's Reaction. Also referred to as Korsakoff's psychosis, this reaction is characterized by memory defects and disorientation. Terrifying auditory hallucinations are also part of the clinical picture. The differentiating sign is that the patient seems unable to remember anything told to him, even for a few minutes. It is typical of him, however, that he will give some sort of answer—any answer—in an effort to cover up his mnemonic defect; in so doing, he will accept suggestions readily, no matter how untrue or ludicrous they may be. His personality is usually that of a jolly, childish person.

Treatment of Alcoholism. Several modalities are available for the treatment of alcoholism, the prime objective of all being the uncompromising termination of the habitual use of intoxi-

cants. Of late, however, the suspicion has grown that such therapeutic regimens are only palliative, and that deep-lying mechanisms within the alcoholic's psyche must be sought out. It is
true, of course, that the palliative or symptomatic approach is
indispensable, but it cannot be accepted as the final solution
to alcoholism. The predicament of the alcoholic is not unlike
that of a person suffering headaches due to faulty vision; aspirin
may relieve the pain but the sufferer cannot give up the drug
until he has been fitted with proper eyeglasses.

MEDICAL TREATMENT. Institutionalization may be required in
serious cases, if only to get the patient on his feet and on the
road to therapy. His physical health must be supported by a
well-rounded diet, exercise, and sufficient rest. Tranquilizing
agents may be needed for the anxious and "jittery" victim.
Drugs such as antabuse, which discourage the patient from drinking, are effective, but unless someone stands over the patient to
make sure that he takes the drug regularly he will fail to do
his part and will immediately revert to drinking. Antabuse is to
the alcoholic what insulin is to the diabetic—it is a check but
not a cure.

PSYCHOTHERAPY. Because it is the personality imperfection and
emotional immaturity of the alcoholic that demand the intoxicant as a solvent for life's problems and the quasi-adjustment this
may afford, it should be obvious that psychotherapy must be a
part of the treatment if any lasting improvement is to be achieved.
The psychotherapist does not, however, work alone. He has
recourse to many allies. First and foremost there is the organization known as "A. A." (Alcoholics Anonymous), created a quarter
of a century ago by an Ohio surgeon (a compulsive drinker) and
his friend, a New York stockbroker. The A. A. program (which
includes the principle of group therapy, re-education, etc.) has
proved to be the greatest step forward in the struggle against
alcoholism.

THE CHANGE IN RELIGIOUS ATTITUDE. An active role has also
been played by religion, with ministers, priests, and rabbis working in close co-operation with the medical profession. The somewhat heavy moralistic pastoral counseling of the past has undergone a wholesome change. Once the alcoholic was condemned
from the altar as a sinner beyond salvation; now religion acknowl-
edges he is a sick person with the potential for a better and richer

life. Says Dr. Donald W. Hewitt, chief medical adviser for the Los Angeles Charity Alcoholic Rehabilitation Center: "The physician can refer the alcoholic to someone who will reassure his patient that God is a loving and forgiving Father who is willing to blot out and forgive the sins if the alcoholic is only contrite and repentent (that is, if he has 'insight'). . . . An alcoholic is already suffering truly excruciating physical and mental anguish. Portraying God as a stern, unrelenting Deity who demands His 'pound of flesh' for each sin committeed will often load down the alcoholic with what he feels is an unsupportable burden that only further drinking can ease for him."

THE KEYSTONE OF THE TREATMENT PROGRAM. Increasing experience and sociological research on the subject of alcoholism indicate the trends that are taking place and the further steps to be adopted in tackling the problem of alcoholism:

1. Alcoholism is a community, not merely an individual, matter. Consequently, it is the family that should be treated. Promising results have been obtained at Johns Hopkins Hospital, where alcoholics and their wives (or husbands) have undergone group therapy concurrently.

2. Prevention is far more to be preferred than treatment. School programs are beginning to adopt a reasonable and effective presentation on the subject of alcohol use and abuse. Such a presentation should be an integral part of every education program.

3. Excellent results have been attained from such group therapy centers as the one at Central Islip State Hospital, Long Island, New York, but additional centers are urgently needed.

4. Research efforts—statistical, physiological, pharmaceutical, sociological, and psychological—must be increased. Indications that this aim is being accomplished to some degree are found in greater state and Federal budgetary grants, and in the continued efforts of the Yale University Center on Alcohol Studies, the National Council on Alcoholism, and the National Institute of Mental Health, among others.

NARCOTISM

Statistics are conflicting as to the number of drug addicts in the United States. The Federal Bureau of Narcotics has established the total to be some 60,000, but others believe that this is much too conservative. A Senate Judiciary Committee investigation has accepted an estimate of 150,000.

Two peculiarities of drug addiction as a social problem do stand out rather prominently in the figures. One is that drug addiction may well be on its way to becoming ethnologically one-sided. Roughly three out of five addicts are Negroes and, according to the U. S. Public Health Service Hospital for drug addicts in Lexington, Kentucky, the percentage of Negro patients in that institution rose from 8.9 in 1936 to 52 in 1955. This is indeed a startling statistic when one realizes that Negroes make up but 11 per cent of the nation's total population. The other peculiarity is the youth-centered nature of narcotism.

Marijuana—the Spark Plug. One of the more serious aspects of the narcotic problem is the fact that one drug is physically harmless and is not even habit-forming! That drug is marijuana. The only pathologic result of its habitual use that has been demonstrated in a large number of users is an optical condition, photophobia (exaggerated sensitivity to light), which makes it necessary for the sufferer to wear dark glasses at all times.

In the strict sense of the word, marijuana is not regarded as habit-forming. Unlike the other drugs mentioned here, it does not develop an increasing and unshakable craving in the user; he can dispense with it at will whenever he pleases. However, marijuana often serves as an introduction to a drug with a greater "kick"—principally heroin. In this lies the insidious effect of marijuana; it renders the individual easy prey for the "pushers" (vendors) of drugs which are habit-forming.

Another ensnaring feature of marijuana is its ready accessibility. Unlike the other drugs, which must be smuggled into the country, this weed can be grown without any special horticultural knowledge anywhere in the world. It has been found in fields, in vacant lots, in window-sill flowerpots, and in tin cans on fire escapes.

Customarily smoked in cigarette form, marijuana produces mental exaltation, intoxication, and certain strange sensations—double consciousness, disturbance of time and space appreciation, and a false impression of performance efficiency. Reports of marijuana users who, with little previous training, played musical instruments or danced skillfully while under the influence of the drug are entirely unfounded. Microcosmic and macrocosmic experiences have been commonly described; in the former state, the individual has the impression that he is so large that he may knock over objects or step on people if he moves; in the latter state, everything and everyone about him seem enormous.

The Habit-forming Drugs. Cocaine, heroin, morphine, and opium have almost identical actions and effects owing to their fundamental pharmacochemical relationship, i.e., they are alkaloids. These are a large group of organic, basic substances found in plants. They are usually bitter in taste and physiologically active. None of them originate in the United States and all must be smuggled into the country through underworld sponsorship. Heroin is chiefly Italian-born; the others are gathered and dried in China and surreptitiously brought into this country either directly or via a number of way stations (Cuba, Mexico, and South America, for example).

COCAINE. Cocaine is an alkaloid obtained from the leaves of *Erythroxylon coca* and other species of *Erythroxylon*. Its local anesthetic qualities were first made known to the medical profession almost a century ago by the eminent ophthalmologist, Carl Koller. There are two major degrees of addiction to the drug: acute cocainism and chronic cocainism.

Acute Cocainism. After an initial brief giddiness and slight headache, the cocaine user is imbued with a feeling of euphoria. These reactions are typical responses to sympathomimetic agents (those which affect the sympathetic nervous system), of which cocaine is one. Under the spell of the pathological grandiosity the individual claims he can "accomplish great things"—and frequently he can justify this boast. He attains new heights in his work, speaking and writing fluently and impressively, or performing artistically with great verve, dexterity, and originality. Perhaps the most noteworthy example of this is the case of one of America's immortal surgeons, who inadvertently acquired the cocaine habit while a young man studying in Europe. Ernest Jones tells us, in his biography of Sigmund Freud, that the father of psychoanalysis advised this young man to use cocaine for some current complaint (in those days little was known of the evil effects of addiction to this drug). Until his death—in his eighties —the eminent surgeon remained a slave to cocaine!

After the stage of elation passes, there is a generalized weakness of the mental faculties, along with fatigue, in-co-ordination, and tremulousness. The final clinical picture is that of a morose, irritable, suspicious person who may experience hallucinations. Fatal termination is a possibility, depending on the dosage and the individual resistance.

The acute stage of cocainism is referred to as a "cocaine jag," in which the victim presents dilated pupils, pallor, quickened pulse, elevated blood pressure, and anxiety, all evidences of excitation of the sympathetic nervous system.

Chronic Cocainism. Prolonged use of the narcotic eventually produces a social wreck—an utterly depraved and immoral individual. He neglects every responsibility (job, family, community relations) and becomes completely dissociated from his former role in society. For some yet unexplained reason, male addicts become sexually impotent and their female counterparts resort to perversions. In both there are extreme deterioration, overtalkativeness, and loss of ability to work with the intellect. Memory grows faulty and emotional reactions range from mild overactivity and excited states to sullenness, suspiciousness, irritability, and a snarling, surly manner. The physical stigmata are well known: the patient complains of the "cocaine bug," expressing the feeling that an insect is crawling under his skin and producing intense itchiness, which compels him to claw at himself constantly. He is always sniffing, as if he were perpetually detecting unpleasant odors. The signs of sympathetic excitation become more marked as the addiction progresses: dilated pupils, dry mucous membranes, thirst, a generalized sense of malaise, and cardiac palpitation.

THE OPIUM DERIVATIVES. Opium is the air-dried juice from unripe capsules of *Papaver somniferum* or *Papaver album*. Morphine, discovered in 1806 by Sertürner, is a colorless or white crystalline alkaloid derived from opium. Heroin is a diacetyl form of morphine. In the form in which heroin is used it is chemically known as heroin hydrochloride. As in the case of cocainism, there are two phases of opiumism (morphinism)—acute and chronic.

Acute Opiumism (Morphinism). The classical description of opiumism appeared in De Quincey's *Confessions of an Opium Eater*. At first there are euphoria, a disinclination to move about, and an obsession with rich fantasies, finally giving way to sleep punctuated by lurid dreams. Emerging from his slumber, the addict experiences a sense of heaviness and lethargy. Rarely is the victim excited or depressed.

Chronic Opiumism (Morphinism). Eventually, the opium or morphine addict presents a picture of emotional and intellectual deterioration. He is feeble, emaciated, anemic, and debilitated— a shadow of his former self. His complexion is sallow, his pupils are constricted, he exhibits tremors, and his sensitivity is lowered. Always revealing are the marks of the hypodermic needle here and there on the body, indications that the drug has been taken in what addicts call "the main line." He is impotent, complains of bizarre skin sensations, and may develop extreme symptoms of paranoia. In some individuals an acute delirious reaction may develop.

HEROINISM. Both the acute and the chronic phases of heroinism closely parallel those of opiumism. Possibly because "H" is less expensive than opium or morphine, or because its importation into the United States from Italy has proved so lucrative an enterprise for underworld figures with contacts in that country, heroin has become Public Enemy Number One in the battle against narcotic addiction.

Comparison of Alcoholism and Narcotism. We have seen in the previous pages how addiction is an attempt to evade responsibilities which the patient is unable to face. In withdrawing from life situations, the addict to either alcohol or drugs is actually regressing to a point in his infancy where all his needs could be satisfied orally. The inadequate personality development which renders an individual unable to accept reality is a basic weakness, and because of this faulty development the individual feels the need of some stimulating or elevating drug or intoxicant to blot out his problems—to make him "forget." While both alcoholics and narcotic users show similar personality structures, there are marked differences between the two types of addiction regarding the individuals affected, the social implications, and the attitudes toward treatment. Below are listed some of these major points of comparison.

APPEAL OF NARCOTICS. A Federal Bureau of Narcotics survey recorded 60 per cent of all drug addicts as being between twenty-one and thirty years of age, and 12 per cent under twenty-one, showing that nearly three quarters of these addicts are adolescents or young adults. This is the striking difference between narcotism and alcoholism. The latter occurs chiefly in persons in their later years, the former claims younger individuals. Why this should be so is not easy to explain. It would appear that the maladjusted adolescent (or recent adolescent) in the grip of a narcotic is usually one who, quite early in life, was consumed by the feeling that he had "two strikes against him," perhaps stemming from a broken home or other serious neglect; or he may be the individual who, in the face of overwhelming frustration, has developed a hostile attitude toward authority, and consequently is resentful of even the mildest social restriction.

On the other hand, the alcoholic, approaching the twilight of life, is haunted by the realization that he has "missed the boat" in a number of ways (marital maladjustment, dissatisfaction with career, absence of adventure), has failed to attain his goals, or has generally "made a mess of things." He is afraid of failure, afraid to face reality, but usually lacks the drive to try for the lurid thrills derived from being "hopped up," and prefers to drown his disgust and feelings of futility in a less cataclysmic manner.

ATTITUDE TOWARD TREATMENT. Another striking difference between alcoholism and narcotism lies in the addict's attitude toward and the results of treatment. While the drug addict seeks treatment much more readily than does the alcoholic, the latter is more likely to be cured of his addiction.

Invariably, the narcotic's quest for treatment has behind it a deliberate plan to reconstitute himself so that he can begin the cycle of addiction all over again—motivation for therapy based solely on economics: as the craving for drugs demands higher and higher dosage, the greater the financial burden becomes for the addict. The alcoholic, however, develops so low a tolerance to intoxicating beverages that he can almost be said to be "allergic" to them. As time goes by, he loses his discriminating taste for the better liquors and will accept the cheapest brands, then will take to using substitutes (hair tonics, cough medicines, etc.), and eventually one meets the canned heat (Sterno) habitué. In this sense, the alcoholic is in a sorrier state than is the drug addict, for he can continue to feed his addiction at very low economic levels, whereas the narcotic user requires a bigger and bigger dose.

Economic Factors. Finally, there is a socioeconomic difference between alcoholism and narcotism that makes the latter a far more serious problem. It resembles somewhat the comparison between arithmetic and geometric progression. Let us say that the need for and the consumption of alcohol proceeds arithmetically; the supply is abundant and the cost within reason, and for a great number of persons the craving can be deferred, for a time at least. Contrariwise, the craving of the narcotic addict is far more compelling and the desired drug is an exceedingly rare, illicit, and expensive item. The individual who is "hooked" becomes frenzied in his efforts to obtain a supply of his narcotic, and the deeper he sinks into addiction, the more intense is his need and the greater become his requirements. Destitution often propels him to delinquent or downright criminal acts against society in an effort to obtain the wherewithal to satisfy his needs.

Combined Alcohol and Narcotics. Can a person be addicted to *both* liquor and drugs? From what has been described it would seem that such a combination is out of the question. However, among the young, in the drive for a "lift," the early stages of drinking or the imbibition of low percentage alcoholic beverages —the phase of "stimulation" as opposed to the depressive stage of heavy and constant drinking—are combined with mood-elevating drugs. Thus, benzedrine (amphetamine), which resembles adrenalin but possesses a greater ability to stimulate the higher brain centers, is mixed with cheap domestic wine by thrill-seeking youngsters. This potent concoction—the "bennie"—is, unfortunately, easy to obtain and very cheap. Case histories of drug addicts very often reveal that the bennie is the first step on the stairway to heroin addiction.

Treatment of Narcotism. The problem of devising an effective means of fighting the drug addiction situation remains essentially unsolved. It has spilled over the bounds as a medical challenge and has become of major interest to sociologists, jurists, penologists, police officials, and others. One reason for this is the lack of concurrence on therapeutic programs. Even within the same discipline there are strong adherents of diametrically opposite regimens. It is possible that this widespread disagreement stems from a seemingly vain attempt to develop a permanent cure. There have been strikingly successful instances of recoveries, as in the case of Barney Ross, the ex-Marine hero and former prize fighter. Ross gained excellent insight into his condition and has since devoted most of his time to delivering lectures on the vices of narcotism. But such cases are rare and receive attention only because the person involved is a public idol.

In spite of what was said previously concerning the contrast between the alcoholic and the narcotic addict in his attitude toward treatment, not every addict seeks therapy. Unfortunately some prominent persons, especially in the entertainment world, who capture the imagination of large blocs of the population, have sufficient funds to keep themselves in a semiadjusted state. Consequently, they loom as models for youthful persons who long to "live with a thrill." Added to this is the fact that there is no statute by which an addict can be forcibly institutionalized for treatment; such incarceration is regarded as a violation of the individual's basic constitutional rights. As was formerly noted, while many addicts do seek treatment, it is not a cure they are after, but improvement to the point where they can return to the small dosage that is within their financial means.

Three methods of treatment for narcotic addiction are presently used: immediate and total withdrawal, gradual and partial withdrawal, and the "British plan."

IMMEDIATE AND TOTAL WITHDRAWAL. Among chronic users of narcotics, this method is known as "cold turkey." Anyone who has witnessed this horrible—sometimes fatal—sequence of physiological and psychological events has been visibly shaken by the patient's maniacal behavior and physical torture. He is restless, complains of chills and "hot flashes," has excessive nasal secretion, and shouts that he is suffocating. He experiences severe abdominal cramps and "dragging" pains in the legs, perspires profusely, and shakes violently. Vomiting and diarrhea rack his gastrointestinal system. He may "see double." Male sufferers have seminal emissions and females experience orgasms. The patient alternates between pleading for "just one more shot," weeping, begging on his knees, and threatening, shrieking, and cursing, while beating his fists on metal bars. Eventually he collapses.

The foregoing state may last for two or three days after the withdrawal regimen is started. By this time medical aid may be unable to preserve his life. If he does survive, vigorous measures are instituted to restore him to good health.

GRADUAL AND PARTIAL WITHDRAWAL. Under this program of slow and incomplete reduction of narcotic dosage, the patient, with supervision, receives his customary drug in decreasing quantities, and non-habit-forming sedatives are substituted in increasing amounts. A variation of this method employs somewhat faster withdrawal while the patient is subjected to vigorous replacement of vitamins and minerals and a high caloric diet. Fluids are maintained at a high level for several days. At the beginning of this treatment program the patient is usually un-co-operative and may have to be fed intravenously.

THE "BRITISH PLAN." This therapeutic program has stirred up heated controversy. In England narcotics are provided to addicts, free of cost—but only if they agree to undergo and continue to follow psychotherapy until the physician decides the treatment may be discontinued. The philosophy behind this scheme is the belief that the narcotic trade, with all its underworld accompaniments, would thus be deprived of its income and collapse and, as a consequence, the root of this evil would be stamped out.

Regardless of the method of treatment used, it is generally agreed by all concerned that psychotherapy must be included in the program if there is to be any lasting improvement. The addict to either alcohol or narcotics has tried to escape, through whichever form he chooses, from the reality of his problems. He must be brought back, through psychotherapy, to a recognition of these problems, and must be helped to make an adjustment to his environment before permanent recovery can be expected, or even hoped for.

11: Mental Retardation

At the halfway mark of the twentieth century the term "mental retardation" began to take the place of "mental deficiency," which had earlier replaced "feeble-mindedness." This semantic shift came in response to two developments. First, both professional and lay groups (in particular, parents of retarded children) reached the conclusion that the concept of "deficiency," implying faulty heredity, was an unwarranted stigma. Second, the older phrase, suggesting an innate, ineradicable defect that permanently limited the individual's development, placed unjustified stress on a hopeless outlook. As it became apparent that much could be done to improve the lot of these unfortunate people, and a wide range of conditions began to be categorized under "mental deficiency," the concept of retardation gained favor, and now it is generally accepted as the accurate, comprehensive term for the conditions described in this chapter.

Mental retardation does not refer solely to intellectual inadequacy and its accompanying social maladaptability, but includes *any* "slowed mind." The condition may be seen in a withdrawn and preoccupied psychotic, a befuddled alcoholic, a drug addict, or an introspective neurotic, as well as in the mongoloid idiot or the "moron." With respect to children, the new, broader clinical concept of retardation has led to increased stress on the clinical concept of the *autistic child,* which is discussed later in this chapter.

The American Association on Mental Deficiency defines feeble-mindedness, or mental retardation, as "including all degrees of mental defect due to arrested or imperfect mental development, as a result of which the person so afflicted is incapable of competing on equal terms with his normal fellows or of managing himself or his affairs with ordinary prudence."

PREVALENCE OF MENTAL RETARDATION

It is estimated that 3 per cent of the American population is mentally deficient. However, if "borderline" intelligence is included (I.Q. 70–75), that figure becomes 4 per cent. It is amazing, nevertheless, that only three one-hundredths of 1 per cent of mental defectives of *all* grades are institutionalized! It is interesting to note how this hospitalized group is distributed in the three categories of mental deficiency (considering intelligence level only for this immediate discussion), because an appreciation of this clinical-statistical phenomenon must influence the approach to therapy, on which lay and medical authorities differ, as we shall see. The distribution of the hospitalized retarded is as follows:

I.Q. Range	% of Total Hospitalized
0–19	30
20–49	50
50–70	20

Note that in the United States every five minutes a mentally retarded infant is born.

The broader concept of mental retardation is more easily appreciated when we consider the nine known causes of defective intelligence. The most superficial scanning of the following list will reveal that the range of causative factors is wide and that it includes features in effect before, during, and after birth; mechanical, bacterial, and traumatic influences; and the still unknown elements of heredity and metabolism.

1. Prenatal Developmental Disorders. "Faulty embryotrophy," which refers to passing developmental mishaps and toxic infections occurring during pregnancy, has long been neglected by researchers. Of late, however, it has become the center of investigations into maternal prenatal illnesses, particularly the "exanthemata" (those diseases characterized by skin eruptions, such as measles, chicken pox, etc.). It is clinically known that these acute illnesses, most commonly encountered in childhood, frequently affect the white matter of the brain and lead to permanent, organic damage (e.g., encephalitis). There is accumulating evidence that a sizable number of mentally defective children can have their retardation traced to mothers who, early in pregnancy, suffered the acute diseases mentioned previously.

The commonest prenatal developmental disorder (and malformation) seen in mentally defective individuals is *hydrocephalus (hydro,* water + *kephale,* head). Here, faulty development of the blood-cerebrospinal fluid septum results in the accumulation of fluid within the brain of the victim and the consequent separation of the skull's bones. The invariable termination—at a very early age—is the fatal "bursting" of the brain within the cranium. Mental deficiency in hydrocephalus "mechanically" results from the dammed up and ever increasing fluid pressing more and more on brain tissue and atrophying (shrinking) that organ until there is complete cessation of function. A hydrocephalic child seldom lives to its fourth birthday.

Other developmental malformations include microcephaly (small head), oxycephaly (so-called "pin" or "sugar cone" head), and porencephaly (cysts or cavities in the brain). Conditions such as anencephalia (absence of brain) and cyclopia (one eye and fused ventricles of the brain) are not compatible with life.

2. Encephalomalacia. Literally meaning, "soft brain," this category includes the wealth of injuries that result in deformities and mental deficiencies seen at birth. These injuries and defects may be manifested in many ways. Some of the clinical entities, such as infantile congenital hemiplegia ("half-stroke," i.e., paralysis of one side of the body), closely resemble adult syndromes. It is not known how much influence a fortuitous combination of genes exerts, or to what extent an inexplicable intrauterine shift or change may convert an otherwise healthy embryo into a faulty one.

3. Congenital Mental Deficiency. The most frequent condition contributing to intelligential inadequacy is *mongolism.* It occurs in 10 to 25 per cent of all cases of mental deficiency.

It was Dr. J. Langdon Down of London who, in 1866, named those infants whose facial characteristics resemble the Oriental so remarkably. Recently, in seeking the cause of mongolism, research has been focusing on the hypothesis that faulty functioning of sex glands, the thyroid, and the suprarenals, under the "leadership" of the pituitary, may be at fault, thereby preventing normal growth and development. It is also thought possible that during pregnancy the mother may fail to produce hormonal secretions adequately or properly, owing, perhaps, to her age, or poor physical health. No mongoloid woman has ever become pregnant, a fact which seems to substantiate this theory. Until recently, mongoloid babies ("like" mongols, but less severely so), died at an early age, chiefly because of their vulnerability to infection. Contrary to popular opinion, mongoloids can live to a ripe old age. At the Vineland School in New Jersey one such patient at the time of this writing was in his seventy-seventh year. With the advent of antibiotics the majority of mongoloids are now living to adulthood, and psychiatry is only beginning to discover the extent to which these people can be taught or trained.

There are several other characteristics which mark a mongoloid individual other than the typical Mongolian features. The small skull is flattened in the rear, the hair is dry and sparse, and the tongue is large and fissured and usually hangs from the open mouth. Hands are squat and broad, the fifth finger being unusually short and curved inward. Limbs seem rubbery because of poor control or complete lack of control over muscles and ligaments. Genitalia are small, the abdomen large, and the palate often deformed. The mongol child is very affectionate, imitative, and jolly in disposition.

4. Metabolic Disorders. Such clinical entities include several conditions that are extremely rare. The commonest is *amaurotic family idiocy* or *Tay-Sachs disease,* a disorder characterized by blindness, paralysis, mental deficiency, and a cherry-red spot on the *macula lutea* of the eye (within the orbit and seen only with an ophthalmoscope). Such an infant seldom lives to two years.

5. Disease of the Endocrines. The outstanding example of this cause of mental retardation is the failure of the thyroid gland to function adequately, resulting in *cretinism.* In addition to the physical signs—thin, strawlike hair, brittle nails, dry, thick skin, puffy face, and large lips—there is mental deficiency to a degree that the child never reaches a level higher than imbecility.

6. Tumor. Here, the implication is "multiple" growths, usually seen as nodules. An example of this group is *tuberous sclerosis,* characterized by small lumps under the skin in various parts of the body, convulsive seizures, and mental deficiency.

7. Trauma (Injury). Before, during or after birth, trauma resulting in brain damage may produce mental deficiency, depending on the site and extent of the brain involvement. The presence or absence of a permanent lesion as opposed to a transient, reversible one, very often determines the extent to which the brain will be affected.

8. Infection. As in the case of trauma, damage to the brain by infection (prenatal or postnatal) may result in mental deficiency; the effects depend upon the extent to which the brain is involved. Bacterial provocation has been decreasing, of course, as more specific antibiotics have entered the arena of medical therapeutics.

9. Heredodegenerative Diseases. As the designation implies, these destructive brain conditions are inherited. One example is *Schilder's disease* (*encephalitis periaxilis diffusa*) in which there is progressive brain degeneration, clinically manifested by visual failure, mental deterioration, and spastic (rigid) paralysis. Certain infections can also be heredodegenerative—maternal syphilis is a condition of this nature, in which the infant is infected during pregnancy and is born with the disease. This disease is evidenced at birth by the yellow, hypertrophied, fatty appearance of the placenta (afterbirth); the diagnosis is corroborated by a blood Wassermann test. Thanks to intensive antibiotic therapy, considerable clinical success has been achieved, and juvenile syphilis, particularly juvenile paresis, is seen infrequently in younger children.

10. Unknown Causes. Finally, there are many cases of mental retardation in which there is no tangible, identifiable cause. These are said to be "idiopathic," or of unknown etiology.

INTELLIGENCE

Mention of "intelligence" and "mental deficiency" immediately brings to mind the popular term "I.Q." It is commonly assumed that intelligence tests are the *sine qua non* in measuring mental capacity. However, while they are useful diagnostic aids, they are not scientifically precise or specific, and they serve merely as a guide for the psychiatrist. Too often an I.Q. is disproportionate to the total clinical picture. For example, there is a type of mental deficiency known as *idiot savant* in which an imbecile or moron (in terms of I.Q. standards) has an unusual adeptness in one particular field of endeavor, such as automobile repair work, fixing watches, etc. Thus, a therapy program for a retarded child can never be based solely on the results of I.Q. measurements.

The prime element in defective mentality is a deficiency in or an alteration of *intelligence,* a term that may be defined as "the general capacity of the individual to adjust his thinking to new and unexpected requirements (which he encounters) in the environment." Intelligence is contrasted with *instinct,* which may be defined as "the innate capacity to cope with environment." Intelligence depends on memory, association of ideas, perception, and execution.

Intelligence tests may, in a general way, indicate whether the individual is subnormal, normal, or above average in intelligence. The most widely employed test is the Terman-Stanford Revision of the Binet-Simon Scale (originated in France) which is an effective means of measuring the mental capacity of children of school age. In testing adults, the Wechsler-Bellevue Intelligence Scale has been of considerable value. It should be remembered, however, that such measures of intelligence refer to the relative standing of one individual in comparison with others in a large group; social adjustment is equally important. As Binet and Simon, the originators of modern intelligence testing, stated: "A peasant, normal in ordinary surroundings, may be considered a moron in the city."

In addition to a great variety of tests generally applied, there are special tests for children under the age of three. *Performance tests* are available for various age groups, while *mechanical tests* have been created for use both with children and adults and particularly with blind, deaf, and un-co-operative patients. There are also less intensive tests which measure the individual's reading ability, skill in manipulating blocks, mastery of vocabulary, etc., in order to determine his I.Q.

IDENTIFICATION OF MENTAL RETARDATION

Dr. Clarence Potter has established the following criteria for the identification of mental deficiency:

1. Is the patient socially inefficient? (Is he a child who cannot adapt himself to routine or to the school situation? Is he an adult who exhibits antisocial behavior, etc.?).

2. Does this socially ineffective state depend on maladjusted intelligence?

3. Has this maladjusted intelligence originated during the developmental period of life?

The answers to these three questions assist the psychiatrist in determining not only whether the patient is mentally defective, but also to what extent that condition may prevent his potential social adjustment. On the basis of such analysis a long-range program of therapy and training can be individualized.

Certain symptoms are common to most types of mental deficiency, and these may be considered under the four headings of mental symptoms, physical symptoms, endocrinopathies, and neurological signs and symptoms.

1. Mental Symptoms. Common to mental defectives are the following symptoms:

> Faulty comprehension.
> Poverty of ideas.
> Weak, illogical reasoning.
> Immature foresight.
> Superficiality of observation.
> Emotional immaturity.

More individualized symptoms are:

> Delay and retardation in motor functioning and growth.
> Delay in acquisition of speech.
> Faulty integration of activities (i.e., failure to respond to environmental stimuli).
> Play ineffectiveness—at first with toys, later with other children.
> Delay in acquiring habits of personal hygiene, eating, social behavior, and cleanliness.
> Secondary personality reactions due to the child's feeling that he is different from others (inferiority): shyness and timidity and behavior reactions which occur as "compensation for the inability to learn."

2. Physical Symptoms. These include:

> Flaring, patternless ears.
> Congenital cataracts.
> Defective palatal arch.
> Irregularly erupting teeth.

Spina bifida (congenital failure of the spinal canal to close
which causes the cord to herniate beneath the skin), or
spina bifida occulta (partial failure of the spinal cord to
close, in which case a true herniation has not occurred).
Ocular imbalances.
Congenital heart defects.
Horseshoe kidneys.

3. Endocrinopathies. In these cases, dwarfism, unusual obesity,
scaly skin, thin, brittle hair, or various other symptoms may be
present, depending on which endocrine glands are affected (pituitary, suprarenals, thyroid, etc.).

4. Neurological Signs and Symptoms. These include muscular
weakness, palsied limbs, pathological gait, changes in reflexes,
alteration in sensation, disequilibrium, etc.

Parents should know that certain emotional states, resulting in
intellectual deficiency may be mistaken for mental defectiveness.
For example, *strephosymbolia* is a reading defect in which a child
fails to learn to read in response to traditional classroom methods.
This is not "word blindness" (*alexia*) in which a neurological
lesion actually destroys the "reading center" in the brain, but an
outward expression of an inner conflict in which letters "mean
to a child what a Chinese laundry ticket means to us," to quote
Doctor Potter. "Word deafness" is a similar condition based on a
like emotional situation. The child is not organically deaf; he
hears everything that is said, but the words are meaningless to
him. Thus, he may hear, "Please close the door," and respond
by tying his shoelace or, more commonly, simply stare at his
questioner.

TYPES OF MENTAL RETARDATION

There are three levels of mental deficiency or retardation:
idiot, imbecile, and moron. We shall differentiate among these
categories and explore the capabilities and limitations of each.

An *idiot,* as the term is defined by the American Psychiatric
Association, "is unable to guard himself against common physical
dangers." Low-grade idiots cannot be trained; high-grade idiots
may be taught very simple procedures, such as toilet habits. However, they cannot learn to dress or bathe themselves. They com-

prehend only the simplest commands. Many of them, because of congenital paralysis or muscular weakness, cannot even sit up and must be spoon-fed. At most, their speech consists of a few articulate words. Some idiots are very restless, noisy, and destructive; others lie immobile in bed, staring vacantly at the ceiling. Most idiots maintain some type of endless, stereotyped movement, such as swaying on their haunches or twisting the head rhythmically from side to side.

An *imbecile* is defined as a person who "is able to guard himself against common physical dangers, or can be taught to do so, but cannot profit from ordinary teaching." In some instances, a high-grade imbecile can learn to read a few monosyllabic words, assist in simple work, and wash and dress himself. He cannot, however, support himself economically. Although they are generally pleasant, very affectionate, and faithful, imbeciles lack the innate curiosity and spontaneous vivacity of normal children of the same chronological age.

A *moron* is often able to progress slowly through the lower grades of elementary school. Sometimes a high-grade moron may reach high school before his intelligential handicap is detected. Morons can learn to perform simple, routine tasks such as errands, distributing leaflets from house to house, washing cars, etc. Too often their suggestible and undeveloped minds are capitalized upon by criminals who can easily train them to be killers. Morons are generally sullen and sulky, easily irritated, but very responsive to flattery and gifts.

Psychometric classification of mental retardation, an arbitrary delineation at best, is as follows:

TYPE	I.Q. (CHILDREN)	MENTAL AGE
Idiot (Severe)*	Less than 20 (acutely retarded)	Less than 3 years (totally dependent)
Imbecile (Moderate)*	20–49 (moderately retarded)	3 years to 7 years 11 months (trainable)
Moron (Mild)*	50–69 (mildly retarded)	8 years to 10 years 11 months (educable)

* Degree of mental retardation

The institutionalization of idiots is twenty-five times greater than that of imbeciles, and the proportion of the latter in institutions is fifteen times greater than that of morons. From this it is obvious that it is not mental retardation *per se* that leads to institutionalization, but the inability to adjust to the outside world. The overwhelming bulk of the hospitalized mental defectives is composed of acutely and moderately retarded groups. They present, primarily, somatic and psychological handicaps. Only a very minute number are in institutions for academic training. This, then, is the irrefutable answer to well-meaning but uninformed groups who believe the panacea for institutionalized defectives is special education. This belief has prompted misguided organizations to fight attempts of state mental health departments to change the name of "state school" to "state hospital and school," in recognition of the need for integrated medical, neurological, and psychiatric care for nine-tenths of all patients.

Even some doctors are responsible for uninformed attitudes toward retarded children. Psychiatrists justifiably resent the point of view taken by obstetricians and pediatricians who exhort mothers, upon delivery of mentally defective infants, to "put them away and forget them." Dr. Clemens E. Benda has commented on the consequences: "When one of these mothers is summoned months or years later to the institution because of her child's critical condition, or need for surgery, etc., she invariably exclaims: 'Is this what I was told is a monster—this pretty, lovable child who happens to lack normal intelligence?' And, very often, such a mother, in reaction to guilt for rejection of her baby, suffers an emotional or psychic disorder."

This point of view is particularly applicable in the case of a mongoloid infant. If the baby's mongolism is the sole psychic and physical handicap, it will fare far better with its mother, for a mongoloid does not require more or different care than a normal baby. On the other hand, if institutionalization were an absolute necessity, in New York City alone, with 400 such births annually, an institution of 2,000 beds, exclusively for mongoloids, would have to be erected every five years!

THE AUTISTIC CHILD

In the recent past it has proven clinically wise in diagnosing and treating children, to give careful consideration to the effects of *autism*. "Autistic thinking" attempts to gratify unfulfilled desires without due regard for reality. Objective reality is distorted, obscured, even excluded. When an autistic child is withdrawn, regressed, retarded, perhaps "mute," it is quite apparent that such a clinical picture could be the result of a severe psychosis, actual mental deficiency, extreme infection, profound neurotic preoccupation, or one of several other causes. Likewise, since the child cannot (or will not) pay attention, intelligence testing would produce a low I.Q.—regardless of whether the subject is an actual imbecile or a brilliant, but psychotic, child.

Therefore, no autistic child is initially regarded as a mental defective before intensive attempts have been made to uncover and remove other possible causes of the autism. As time goes by, it is becoming increasingly common for the psychiatrist to encounter a child with an I.Q. of 30 who, when the provocative etiology is found and obliterated, presents, on retesting, an I.Q. of 110! Dr. Lauretta Bender, an authority on children's psychological and psychiatric difficulties, states that more and more of these autistic youngsters are proving to be victims of organic brain disease or schizophrenia.

TREATMENT OF MENTAL RETARDATION

Treatment of mental retardation is not the bleak, hopeless task most laymen believe it to be. For example, when mentally defective twins are separated after birth and one of them is exposed to specialized, intensive training and education, he will actually develop an I.Q. higher than his untutored twin. It is true that more can be done with and is expected of the higher-grade defective. Although intellectual capacity cannot be appreciably augmented, treatment can and should aim to make the patient socially adjustable and acceptable. All persons need opportunities to develop intellectually, but possibly even more important are the emotional needs: social recognition, security, love, a chance "to do," and new experiences. Dr. Walter E. Fernald always maintained that the feeble-minded person has a right to have his needs understood and to be treated accordingly, instead of being classified and isolated on the basis of his I.Q.

In planning a therapy program it is recommended by the American Association on Mental Deficiency that all possible clinical data be assembled. These include the patient's present intelligence level, his mental condition, and his emotional reactions to his anatomical, physiological, and neurological constitution. An estimate of his behavior, social adjustment, biological background, and social heredity should be made, and there should be careful consideration of his entire developmental history. Special laboratory and X-ray studies may be indicated. In short, an inventory is made of the patient's physical, mental, and emotional assets. The treatment program capitalizes and exploits these to the utmost.

The treatment of the idiot and the low-grade imbecile consists mainly of custodial and physical care. The low-grade imbecile may profit by training; he can learn to dress, bathe, and feed himself, to avoid ordinary environmental dangers, and to check his destructiveness. Such a training program can be carried out in the home. Furthermore, current programs in this country call for the establishment of centers where mothers can learn how to care for their mentally retarded children. There is no substitute for a mother's love in the raising of any child.

Institutionalization. In the more extreme grades of retardation, institutionalization is not intended as a means of segregating the patient by lifetime incarceration. It is to be regarded as a temporary and fortunate opportunity to expose the child to highly specialized training and education, with a view to creating an adjustable, acceptable, economically and emotionally independent citizen.

In addition to occupational, recreational, and academic opportunities, the institutionalized child is imbued with a sense of pride and self-esteem rather than feelings of inferiority, worthlessness, and rejection. The psychiatrist, psychologist, nurse, attendant, and special therapists display firmness in carrying out the program, but always with sympathy, understanding, compassion, and kindness. Praise and reprimand, reward and check, are given as they are justifiably indicated. In addition to being made to feel that he is a social entity—"somebody"—the child is gradually taught, within his capacity, to adjust to group life with the aim of returning to society. A high-grade moron may not understand the operation of a seesaw in principle, but quickly grasps the idea when he sees two other children, like himself, gleefully working one. From co-operation and adjustment with another child, the patient can progress to larger and larger groups in play, at work, in the classroom and dining hall, and at parties.

On the subject of sterilization, professional opinions vary. The various types of people considered unfit to bear children are not restricted to those with defective intelligence. Sterilization is not an effective means of halting mental retardation, and its usefulness, says Dr. Arthur P. Noyes, "is more individual than racial. Sterilization as a general policy is a superficial method of approaching the problem of feeble-mindedness since it ignores the need for special investigation and research as to its cause and prevention."

Parents should realize that very often it is therapeutically beneficial to place an institutionalized child with adult patients. The older individuals can be "surrogate" parents representing a substitute authority; the child may have failed to "grow up" when in a ward with others of his own age, but with adults he may be emotionally stimulated to relinquish his infantile fixation.

Day Care Centers. It has been pointed out that not every retarded infant requires institutionalization. In any case, whatever is gained by placing a defective baby in a hospital is offset by a loss of his mother's love, care, and attention. Consequently a new concept has entered the field of therapy. This approach makes use of the day care center, where the mother and her infant come, daily, weekly, or at whatever other interval is prescribed. While the child is treated and trained, his mother is oriented and instructed in how to carry out at home what is being done for her infant at the center. Mother and child may be instructed together. This concept carries a strong element of prevention, that is, it aims to avoid institutionalization. It is also a forward step in caring for more patients with less personnel and in a shorter period of time. It is an economic saving for the taxpayer from every aspect. One thing a day care center is not: a place where a mother parks an infant while she follows recreational and shopping pursuits. Finally, it is a medium of education. Personnel from hospitals and social agencies can come to the center to learn how to care for retarded children and to instruct mothers. The long-range result implies use of the day care center in more hospitals and clinics and its extension to churches, welfare agencies, and other comparable institutions.

LOOKING AHEAD

The therapeutic methods currently available to medical science will probably undergo radical alteration as research unearths new approaches in treatment. The chemicophysiological interest that has stimulated psychiatric research so extensively in the recent past is rapidly finding equal enthusiasm in the field of mental retardation. Four promising projects are currently under extensive investigation:

1. *Sedac,* which is a convenient term for "high frequency current" as it is used in spastic children, particularly cerebral palsy victims, is apparently an effective check to the uncontrollable movements and in-co-ordination observed in these children. More time is needed to ascertain whether repeated treatments are required and whether the benefits noted last as long after each treatment.

2. *Chorionic gonadotrophic hormone,* extracted from the urine of pregnant mothers, is being used to change mood and personality defects in mentally retarded boys. The principle behind this treatment is that while the man is aggressive and carries his genital markings externally (scrotum and testes), the woman, essentially nonaggressive, carries her reproductive organs (the ovaries) internally. It was observed that mentally retarded boys who are shy, diffident, seclusive, indifferent, and nonaggressive (before puberty) have a "sliding testicle." In these cases the testis is unusually small and slips back into the groin and even into the abdomen. *Chorionic gonadotrophic hormone,* which stimulates tissue growth, seems to enlarge the testicle and narrow the groin's inguinal ring, thereby keeping the testicle in the scrotum. As this occurs, the boy seems to become extraverted, interested, and lively, and more amenable to education and training.

3. There is considerable thought being given to malnutrition as a potential cause of mental deficiency. At present this factor is under study in the cases of retarded infants who, in addition to reinforced, well-balanced feedings, receive *testosterone,* a hormonal extract. It is too early to render an opinion on this research project.

4. Certain retarded children are found to be suffering from *phenylketonuria,* or *phenylpyruvic acid deficiency,* which is

caused by the failure of one of the body's enzymes to assimilate phenylalanine, a chemical found in protein foodstuffs. Use of a purified, low-phenylalanine diet from which the offending substance has been removed helps to prevent or minimize the disorder if treatment is begun before brain damage occurs. A comparatively simple ferric-chloride diaper test offers an effective technique for mass screening and detection.

12: *Epilepsy*

Epilepsy is one of the oldest afflictions known to man. In about 400 B.C., Hippocrates, the father of medicine, made excellent diagnostic observations of the disorder and some of his therapeutic recommendations were not relinquished until fairly recent times. A disease known to all cultures, epilepsy has stricken many eminent personages throughout history: Julius Caesar, Pitt the Elder, Dostoevsky, and Van Gogh, to mention but a few.

ETIOLOGY OF THE DISEASE

The brain, like any other organ, has both a functional and a physiological purpose. In its work performance it manifests activity by creating actual electric, physical, and chemical evidence of its metabolism. For years we have been acquainted with such phenomena in the heart, the electrical potentialities of which made possible the electrocardiographic recording of that organ's activity and defects of such activity. The discovery of a similar measuring technique, electroencephalography (EEG), went far in giving support to the hypothesis that epilepsy is fundamentally a disturbance in the electrophysicochemical activity of the discharging cells of the brain—a disturbance that may be due to a variety of neurological conditions, particularly those affecting the cerebrum. In contrast, if not in opposition, with respect to "cause," is the psychological point of view, which maintains that epilepsy is the outward expression of a mental and/or emotional disorder.

Moreover, epilepsy is both a symptom and a clinical entity. It is popularly regarded as a disorder of consciousness with or without convulsions. However, as a symptom, epilepsy (known as *Jacksonian epilepsy,* after the famous neurologist, Hughlings-Jack-son) is frequently observed in several well circumscribed, readily diagnosed clinical syndromes. In such instances, Jacksonian epilepsy is "symptomatic," that is, it is part of the total clinical picture. For example, in an individual who is handicapped by a congenital malformation of the brain, epileptic convulsions are extremely common. They are also found in such afflictions of the brain as tumors, blood clots, injury, hardening of cerebral arteries, and syphilis of the central nervous system.

When there is no specific or known etiology or where the cause is beyond scientific means of detection, epilepsy is said to be "idiopathic" (with no known cause). This is the condition that is most frequently encountered, involving about three quarters of a million persons in this country. Seventy-five per cent of cases appear before the age of twenty.

While much controversy persists on the subject of epileptic inheritance, there is no doubt that at least the tendency to the disease is transmitted from an epileptic to his offspring. Drs. F. A. and E. L. Gibbs, sponsors of the EEG, and Dr. W. G. Lennox have demonstrated that a typical epileptic EEG pattern is found in normal children whose parents are epileptic.

TYPES OF EPILEPSY

For centuries, persons who suffered "fits" were the only ones diagnosed as epileptics. Not until fairly recent times did medicine begin to include under this category individuals who, while suffering no convulsive seizures, did manifest, from time to time, alterations in consciousness or posture, both fleeting in nature.

Grand Mal Epilepsy. This is epilepsy with convulsions. There is no regularity to grand mal seizures; a patient may suffer one or more fits a day for several days and then be free of attacks for weeks or months. A typical seizure is ushered in by an "aura" or a warning, in which the patient may feel a tingling or numbness in some part of his body, a chill, or a sudden, transient sensation of nausea—any sensation that he learns by repetition is a harbinger of an attack. Immediately thereafter, he utters a piercing shriek, falls to the ground, and becomes unconscious; his body twitches violently, then suddenly stiffens into steel-like rigidity. In a matter of minutes he is limp, perspiring profusely, and in a deep sleep that may last for minutes to hours. In the interim, he may have bitten his tongue, his lips may be covered with blood-tinged foam, and control of bladder and bowels may have been lost. Too often the patient is overtaken by a grand mal attack before he can protect himself from falling and he may suffer serious injury. When he awakes he is confused ("clouded sensorium") and recalls nothing of the attack.

A patient who suffers one grand mal seizure after another in rapid succession, actually passing from one to the next, is said to be in *status epilepticus*. This calls for prompt and vigorous action to save the patient's life since the exhausting tax on the heart and lungs is readily fatal.

Petit Mal Epilepsy. According to Lennox, petit mal, or non-convulsive epilepsy is observed in three subtypes:

Myoclonic epilepsy, characterized by single jerks of flexor muscles. Consciousness is not lost.

Akinetic epilepsy, recognized in sudden postural loss, or a nodding of the head. The patient may even fall to the floor, but he will get up at once.

Pyknolepsy (true petit mal), which involves momentary immobility, or a few muscular, rhythmic jerks, with several seconds of unconsciousness. This is often so brief as to go unnoticed.

ASSOCIATED CONDITIONS

There are some conditions in which the general clinical picture of epilepsy is seen but the manifestations are relatively mild and not diagnosable as true epilepsy. For instance, an epileptic may develop a psychosis with hallucinations, delusions, and disorientation, closely resembling a schizophrenic reaction. Other similar reactions include psychomotor equivalent, narcolepsy, cataplexy, the epileptic personality, epileptic deterioration, and hysterical or shammed epilepsy.

Psychomotor Equivalent. This is characterized by momentary impairment of consciousness, or by amnesia, with purposeful movements and, at times, with emotional outbursts of abject fear or violent rage. Automatic behavior may occur, such as a fugue (see page 67) or anger up to the point of homicide ("epileptic furor"). There are countless other psychic and emotional variations, but it is the EEG that reveals a typically epileptic pattern, thereby clinching the diagnosis.

Narcolepsy. This is actually a clinical variety of sleep disorder. There is reason to believe that narcoleptics have previously suffered acute epidemic encephalitis (sleeping sickness). Narcolepsy is a sudden, overwhelming, irresistible desire to sleep regardless of where the person is, or what he is doing. It is not syncope (fainting) but natural sleep lasting from seconds to a few minutes. The slumberer can be aroused but promptly falls asleep again. When he awakens he feels refreshed. This bizarre affliction usually affects obese young men who often complain of sexual impotence. The drug amphetamine controls the condition quite satisfactorily.

Cataplexy. This sudden postural loss, usually precipitated by excitement, is related in nature to narcolepsy. During the attack, the patient may be unable to speak although he is completely conscious.

Epileptic Personality. No distinctive trait or traits are found universally in epileptics. However, egocentricity is invariably noted to a marked degree and the person presents antithetic characteristics. Concerning the qualities of the epileptic personality, the late Dr. C. MacPhee Campbell stated: "He preaches religiosity while he steals your watch" and "he works for praise and not for pleasure."

Epileptic Deterioration. This term implies a downhill failure in mental and physical capacities to the point that such a patient ultimately is merely vegetating. It is felt that the deterioration is due to minute cellular changes in the cerebrum. To what extent the condition may be attributable to convulsions, the use of ameliorating drugs, or the psychic trauma pursuant to social and cultural ostracism is not known.

Hysterical (Neurotic) and Shammed Epilepsy. These types must be differentiated from true epilepsy, particularly in military and prison work, where "goldbricking" may be suspected. The hysteric usually has an obvious neurotic history and personality, and the criminal, a long record of delinquencies. In both cases, the succession of incidents of a grand mal seizure is not seen, nor are tongue biting or bowel and bladder incontinence encountered. These patients do not fall where they are likely to sustain injury. Finally, there is the incontrovertible EEG which has removed epilepsy from the pretender's bag of tricks.

TREATMENT OF EPILEPSY

The epileptic should be urged to do everything in moderation— eating, working, playing. He should be encouraged about his potential progress and, while steps are taken to control the seizures, always aiming to eliminate them, he and his family should not be permitted to lose heart. However, no therapy will be of value unless the patient is kept in the best physical health. Alcohol and other stimulants should be avoided. The ketogenic diet (high in fat, low in protein and carbohydrates) frequently benefits children.

Among effective drugs in the treatment of grand mal convulsions are *dilantin sodium, mesantoin,* and *lubrium.* Petit mal responds well to *tridione.* When status epilepticus occurs, anticonvulsant agents are immediately stopped; the patient is given intravenously administered sodium phenobarbital and glucose solution, and spinal fluid is drained. Psychomotor equivalents are treated by *phenurone.* Considerable research is under way with electroshock therapy, in which convulsions are induced as a form of replacement, i.e., substituting a seizure which is "scheduled" so that it occurs "under supervision" for one that may occur at any unpredictable time when the victim may suffer injury and embarrassment. Investigators are also experimenting with supersonic surgery which would remove the portion of the brain's temporal lobe believed to be directly related to epileptic seizures.

There are no special requirements in the treatment of an epileptic patient when the disease is accompanied by a mental disorder. The primary objective in both instances is early control of the attacks, whether they are of the grand mal or petit mal type. To obtain success in this objective is itself of inestimable psychological importance to the patient, regardless of the degree of mental stability he enjoys. It is essential to have his co-operation since he is best qualified to report how frequent and how intense the attacks have been prior to and following the institution of drug therapy. As improvement sets in, the psychiatrist encourages the patient, pointing out that the day of dismal, lonely existence for the epileptic is a thing of the past. Much good can be accomplished through interviews with the patient's family, during which their attitude toward epilepsy can be reoriented in an effort to establish a milieu favorable for the patient's adjustment. When a specific mental disorder complicates the clinical picture of epilepsy, the correct therapeutic approach will be essentially the same as described in Chapter 8.

Industry and commerce should not bar any victim of epilepsy from gainful work (except that of a hazardous nature) whose attacks are either controlled, or who, when a seizure is about to develop, is able to withdraw to a rest room and have his attack "in private," without suffering injury. The earliest example of this arrangement was the retirement room adjacent to the senate rostrum for the use of Julius Caesar. Whenever the emperor became aware of an oncoming convulsion he called a recess and withdrew to this secluded area, remaining there for the duration of the attack.

Some communities do not permit persons suffering epilepsy to hold driving licenses. Others ignore the issue. It seems reasonable to advocate that those patients whose physicians certify they have been free of epileptic attacks of all kinds for two years should be allowed to drive automobiles. Behind this clinical opinion is the observation that, with extremely rare exceptions, the patient whose treatment regimen has successfully eradicated clinical manifestations of epilepsy for two years will, while faithfully following this therapeutic program, continue to be free of attacks.

What is the outlook for the epileptic? Total cure in a few instances has been achieved, to the point where no medication is required. In the vast majority of cases, however, we must consider the result of treatment successful when the patient, as long as he continues his medication, is free of attacks. Epilepsy in these cases is comparable to diabetes; the sufferer can enjoy a long and happy life as long as he religiously follows the treatment program prescribed, reporting to his physician from time to time for any possible changes in therapy that may be indicated.

13: The Formative Years

The psychiatrist who specializes in the treatment of children cannot be regarded in the same light as the pediatrician. To begin with, in the physical, emotional, intellectual, and social spheres, the problems of normal children differ radically from those of normal adults. But there are even greater differences between the psychiatric problems of adults and those of children. True, the behavior disorders and neuroses of both adults and children reveal a faulty emotional adjustment to the environment, but this disequilibrium creates a special problem for the child because it tends to establish patterns for the attitudes and behavior of later life. Some children survive the struggle without psychological mishap; some fall prey to more or less minor emotional trauma; still others develop gross faulty reactions requiring intensive psychotherapy.

The child who presents a psychiatric problem will have reacted to his frustration or anxiety either directly or indirectly. In direct, open behavior, he expresses his hostility by stealing, running away, lying, or some other antisocial activity; such overt responses are called "behavior disorders." In the indirect form of reaction, the child sublimates his rebellion, externalizing his hunger for attention through a neurotic or psychosomatic disorder, such as a tic (involuntary muscle twitch), stammering, bed-wetting ("enuresis"), food dislike, night terrors, or sleepwalking.

CAUSES OF CHILDHOOD MENTAL DISORDERS

The child's response to a trying life situation is prompted by forces arising from within (intrinsic) or by influences coming from without (extrinsic) or sometimes by a combination of both.

The response to intrinsic factors may be somatic; or the reaction may be exclusively psychic, appearing as some form of mental aberration, as in the case of the child who "carries his environmental problems around with him." Extrinsic factors, too, may be physical or psychological. Examples of the former would be an unsatisfactory or ill-kept home or a lack of playground facilities; of the latter, the unsavory atmosphere of a strife-torn family or the child's hostility toward some teacher.

Organic Causes. As in the case of the adult, when a child shows signs of abnormal behavior, a careful examination should be made to determine whether some pathological organic condition is to blame. There may be mental retardation caused by a brain injury; malfunctioning of the endocrine glands, particularly the thyroid or the pituitary; or evidence of damage caused by a brain tumor or abscess, meningitis, juvenile paresis, or encephalitis. (For a full discussion of mental retardation and its organic causes, see Chapter 11.)

Faulty Discipline. In Chapter 1, it was shown how mismanagement of the infant from birth to the age of about two or three (when he "goes out into the world") can be reflected later in the youngster's developing personality. Faulty discipline, ranging from indifference to oversolicitude, is often the precursor of behavioral and emotional difficulties. In seeking the *causes* of a child's psychiatric problem it is therefore of utmost importance to determine whether judicious discipline has been provided, whether the child has been given adequate affection and made to feel secure, whether he has received encouragement for his achievements, and whether he has enjoyed social acceptance both at home and abroad. Satisfactory relationships with parents will be translated into healthy interpersonal relationships in the world at large, and one of the means of achieving this aim lies in the development of self-confidence (within the limits appropriate to his age level) through stimulation of the child's belief in his own capacity. In his associations with his playmates he is certain to experience inferiority in some areas, but if his assets are stressed by his parents he will suffer less trauma from the feelings of inadequacy which are part of life. Clinical experience teaches that the most frequently observed factor underlying psychiatric problems of childhood is an unsatisfactory parent-child relationship.

Excessive Neglect or Solicitude. Any disturbance or distortion of the normal psychological development of the child will produce an "unfinished" segment in his personality. It is unfinished because the child has failed, or has not had the opportunity, to solve the problem, and this incompleteness remains in his unconscious as a prompter of anxiety. Analogous or symbolically similar problems arising in later life arouse the old fear of failure, and the youngster responds with either a behavior reaction or a neurotic syndrome. Often as not, it can be demonstrated that maternal love and guidance were lacking; the parent either did not take the time or did not have the wisdom to teach the child how to respond in a healthy manner. This leaves the young one ill-equipped to face responsibilities and reality. As a result, he persists in a lifelong search for the love and guidance he never received. He will always be the "big kid," and, because of his immaturity, he will fail to achieve effective interpersonal relationships as an adult. The reverse of this situation is the undesirable effect of an excessively doting mother, who can create as much havoc as the neglectful mother by making all the decisions for the child, thus denying him the opportunity to exercise his own judgment. As this individual develops, he will be unable to cope with reality or make decisions without assistance, and will experience severe emotional difficulties during the years of change (see Chapter 14).

Environmental Factors. Environmental influences heavily affect personality development. These include overprotection, neglect, cruelty, hostility, parental mental disorders, alcoholism, disharmony, etc., as well as the effects of overly ambitious parents and interfering grandparents. With regard to "neglect," the baby who is left alone in a crib while his mother is out shopping or visiting friends is every bit as "abandoned" emotionally as the infant whose mother, a busy "career executive," delegates her responsibility to a nursemaid.

Other unfavorable environmental factors include divorce, desertion, death of a parent, a broken home, parental favoritism toward another sibling, sibling rivalry, and the strained relationship between stepparent and stepchild or foster parent and foster child. Later influences may be economic difficulties, community antagonism (because of religion, color, nationality, etc.), and school experience.

Lack of Affection. While faulty management of the oral and anal stages of development and the possible results with regard to personality development have been discussed in detail in Chapter 1, there are other ways by which a child may evidence lack of parental affection. The parent whose attitude toward the world is sadistic, punitive, or fearful, may distort his or her child's personality to the point that the emotion of love is a foreign one. Constant frustration and deprivation lead to future hostility and aggression. The child who feels rejected may become anxious or rebellious and resort to misbehavior as a means of finding love. He may "cover up" his craving for affection by sneering at the idea of love and outwardly present himself as the swaggering, defiant, bullying juvenile delinquent.

TYPES OF CHILDHOOD MENTAL DISORDERS

When a conflict affects a youngster's personality functioning there is seldom the true anxiety, obsessive-compulsive reaction, hysteria, or phobic response that is seen in adult neuroses. The personality difficulties of childhood are commonly expressed as violent temper outbursts, jealousy, anger, and various fears—of the dark, of animals, of lightning—or fears that develop as a result of parental threats and warnings. These are known as *conditioned* fears, in contrast to "internal" phobias or *neurotic* fears which may be externalized by projection onto something or someone in the conscious world. In the latter instance we have the abjectly scared, panic-stricken youngster. By the same token, a prolonged fear state, such as the dread of insecurity arising from overprotection, may be masked by aggressive behavior (as, very often, in the case of the juvenile offender).

The nonorganic mental disorders of childhood are manifested chiefly as behavior disorders, psychosomatic disorders, and personality maladjustments.

Behavior (Conduct) Disorders. Like neuroses, conduct disorders are a protest against a difficult life situation. Here we find perverse sexual activities, criminality, running away, cruelty, truancy, fighting, destructiveness, lying, and disobedience. The child feels no remorse or guilt. Some psychiatrists attribute conduct disorders to parental hostility toward and rejection of the youngster which generate abnormal aggressiveness. A behavior disorder may result from a child's attempt to obtain gratification abroad when it is lacking at home. It may be either a means of trying to neutralize feelings of inferiority and inadequacy or an attempt to achieve independence through aggression and misconduct. The behavior reaction, regardless of cause, is an attempt to master a definite situation—a method of dominating the mother, defying school authorities, fighting social rejection, etc.

Psychosomatic Disorders. An emotional disturbance may be expressed through physical channels (see Chapter 5); these are the illnesses affecting the gastrointestinal tract, the nervous system, and other bodily systems. A notable example is bed-wetting (enuresis) that persists after the second year. Such a youngster is usually excitable, anxious, and shy. His failure to master control may be traced to fear, negativism (resistance), lack of parental training, or, more rarely, the expression of spite or jealousy. Grimaces, tics, blinking, and sniffing are everyday examples of habit spasms. Responsible for these may be rebellion against some environmental irritation or plain imitation of elders. The movement is gradually separated from its original purpose and becomes automatized through the presence of emotional and environmental stress.

Among the psychosomatic disorders affecting verbal expression, stuttering is the most prevalent in childhood. The term is used interchangeably with stammering, although the latter implies a total lack of speech sound and the former a repetition of a letter or a syllable. No specific situation gives rise to stuttering; it is regarded as neurotic in origin. Sometimes other muscular movements (twitching of the cheek muscles, bizarre lip movements, etc.) accompany the speech difficulty. Treatment should not be directed solely toward the stuttering itself, but should include a study of the environmental and emotional factors that may have contributed to the impairment of the ability to speak.

TREATMENT OF CHILDHOOD MENTAL DISORDERS

Seldom if ever can a child be separated from his environment and subjected to psychotherapy as an isolated object of treatment. Lauretta Bender, a specialist in this field, points out that each child differs from the next and no one's particular problems are the same as those of others. She says therapeutic emphasis is on "the child's needs, strivings, and growth tendencies in a social and cultural background." The aim of treatment is reorganization of the personality on a healthful, sound basis with improved emotional adjustment. Whatever factors accounted for hostility, aggression, or insecurity, whatever retarded progress so that the child remained "anchored to his infancy," must be removed to allow normal, growth-promoting relationships to develop.

Orthodox psychoanalysis is ineffectual for children. Older children may respond well to a question and answer procedure. No matter how the situation is met, it is usually advisable to have one or both parents oriented as treatment progresses. A mother and/or father may require simultaneous psychotherapy. Part of the treatment may well be the changing of parental (or sibling) attitudes, and the elimination of the child's rigidity and feeling of rejection to which he is reacting with emotional or behavioral disturbances.

Manipulative or environmental therapy makes it possible for the patient to develop active interests on his own and thus overcome introversion and shyness. Here the therapist makes use of scouting, dancing, hobbies club, camp, and other group activities. Camp, for instance, is an ideal means of separating a child from an overprotective mother.

Generally, therapy for children falls under three headings: the psychobiological approach, therapist-child relationships, and projective techniques.

Psychobiological Approach. Originated by Adolf Meyer, the same pattern is followed with the child as with the adult. Every factor concerned with the patient's problems—physical, environmental, intellectual, emotional, etc.—is scrutinized, and altered when necessary. The child's personality and his constitutional and environmental assets are carefully assayed and inventoried as a basis for therapy.

Therapist-child Relationships. Championed by Frederick H. Allen, this approach operates on the belief that some faulty interpersonal situation, generally the parent-child relationship, has impeded the patient's personality development. Through play and other projective techniques, the child uses his relationship with the therapist and the therapeutic experience as the means of removing the block to the development and use of his personality assets.

Projective Techniques. Oriented along psychoanalytical principles, these methods are commonly employed in the treatment of younger children. Whereas the adult expresses himself verbally and establishes transference with the therapist, the small child expresses himself more easily in play. He regards a group of toys as symbols of environment. Blocks are used to make homes; dolls and soldiers may represent parents, siblings, or other human beings; animals may be domestic pets. The child's emotions find an outlet through the "speech" of play. He may smash a doll, caress a toy cat, snarl angrily at another figure. Play permits the projection of unconscious emotional and personality features. Frustrations are demonstrated, death wishes for a parent are revealed, or hidden desires may be openly expressed. Sometimes, a single, fleeting, but repeated move is the clue to a child's difficulty. For example, the constant removal of one toy soldier from a dozen others exactly like it indicated one child's overwhelming jealousy of, and death wishes toward, an older brother. To the play technique may be added painting and drawing— also excellent media for self-expression.

14: The Years of Change

Three erroneous popular beliefs are associated with the middle years of human existence. These are that change of life implies (1) a factor in living applicable only to females because a vital physiological function ceases, (2) the notion that this period of life automatically commences when a woman awakens on the morning of her forty-fifth birthday, and (3) the assumption that "change of life" is, without exception, a cross of agony that must be borne by her thereafter for months, even years.

Added to this confusion are the synonyms for "change of life." These are presented and defined at this point so that their use in this chapter will be understood. They are as follows:

Menopause. The physiologic cessation of menstruation.

Climacteric. Webster defines this as "a period or point in human life (as, among women, the menopause) in which some great change in the constitution, health, or fortune takes place, or is supposed to be especially likely to occur. The critical periods are thought by some to be the years produced by multiplying 7 by the odd numbers 3, 5, 7, and 9; to which others add the 81st year."

Involution. Gould, in his *Medical Dictionary* defines this as "the period of regression or the process of decline or decay which occurs in the human constitution after middle life."

Note that in these definitions (except for reference to the menopause, of course) no differentiation is made between the sexes; no mention is made of a definite year (Webster simply quotes an old wives' tale that has no scientific substantiation); no indication is made that links any pathology with the change of life. It is obvious that *both* men and women pass through a

151

change of life; that this era occurs somewhere in the forties and fifties; and that the period can be lived through happily and healthfully.

Of all the ages of man, the middle years are the outstanding ones of transition. This is the intermediate stage between adulthood and old age, the twilight of one era and the dawn of another. Victor Hugo observed that forty is "the old age of youth, fifty is the youth of old age." As in any other period of life, the pre-involutional personality, physical status, and emotional equilibrium determine whether an individual will glissade through the middle years or suffer somatic and/or psychic difficulties.

A general behavior pattern of "settling down" cannot be taken as a reliable yardstick of middle age. For some, this "easing off" occurs in early adulthood. On the other hand, many individuals are "eager beavers" and "go-getters" in the later decades of life. Witness the Eleanor Roosevelts, the Konrad Adenauers, the Somerset Maughams.

Natural factors and those evolving out of our civilization create a "turning in" or slowing down of function, capacity, will, and bodily components at different stages in life. Physical strength is generally at a peak in younger years. Here are the athletes, the soldiers, the mountain climbers, the garden enthusiasts, the ditch diggers, etc. Mental vigor, on the contrary, seems to reach its zenith in later life, details and examples of which are cited in Chapter 15 ("The Later Years"). Bearing this variance in mind, we can now consider the physiological factors in the involutional period.

THE PHYSIOLOGY OF THE MIDDLE YEARS

Recognizing that involution is a *"turning in,"* it is understandable that tissue and organ changes are natural, normal indications that a function or functions have either served their bodily purpose or reached a point in metabolic life when they are needed less than in earlier years. Similarly, normal "wear and tear" of an organ or a system, as in a machine, call for rest or mechanical assistance or replacement. This latter concept is reflected in the necessity for walking upstairs carefully rather than taking two steps at a time, the need for bifocal lenses, and the administration of hormones.

While the average layman thinks of the change of life as restricted to the menopause, this is but one of dozens of alterations. Visual acuity diminishes, dental decay and receding gums are commonplace, the hair loses its youthful sheen and pliability, the skin may become dry, and the nails brittle. Physical stamina diminishes; there is a greater need for rest. Various other changes, too numerous and well known to mention, also occur at this time.

Responsible for the decrease or cessation in activity is the slowed functioning of the endocrine glands. The thyroid is an excellent example; its reduced action accounts for dry skin, brittle nails, and loss of lustre in the hair. Throughout the body, as fat and fibrous tissue replace muscle strands, the capacity for physical effort is accordingly lessened. The firm biceps of youth become the flabby upper arm of middle life. The heart, a muscular organ, is likewise affected. There is less myocardial potential available to push blood through less elastic and increasingly sclerotic vessels. No organ or system is exempt from change except the blood. That element normally remains the same from birth to death.

Aging is a process that commences with the first breath of life. Autopsies of month-old babies reveal (at least to a microscopic degree) hardening of the arteries not present in vessels of newborn infants (as evidenced by post-mortem examinations of still-births). But aging does not spell *finis* although it may imply decreased capacity. This is stressed because of the common idea that involution connotes the end of sexual potentiality. Nothing could be further from the truth. The normal production of hormones by ovaries and testes slows; it does not stop. Of course, as in any bodily process, if the abnormal occurs (due to known or unknown cause), then *all* features pertaining to those organs fail. Thus, premature cessation of genital power in women may be manifested not only by loss of potency, but also by reversal of feminine characteristics (marked growth of bodily hair, change of voice, flattening and flabbiness of the breasts, etc.). It must be emphasized that these are *pathological* events, not seen in normal aging. Sexual activity usually continues despite the change of life. In women, this is not infrequently marked by an increase in desire immediately before, during, and after the involution.

Finally, longevity and civilization are affecting the climacteric. To cite one phase, women are undergoing the menopause at a later age. It is no longer an obstetrical oddity that a woman in her fifties is delivered of a normal infant. Cultural factors also have a strong influence. In India a girl of thirteen will marry and be an old woman at thirty-five—an age at which a woman is at the peak of feminine vigor and charm in America.

THE PSYCHOPATHOLOGY OF THE MIDDLE YEARS

For the psychiatrist, the involution may present two kinds of psychic disorders: a neurotic depression or a psychosis. The latter may be manifested as a paranoid reaction or a depression, termed melancholia. Behind these reactions is an unconscious feeling of inferiority, a realization that one is less efficient than in the past, that the journey along the path of life is rapidly reaching a dead end. There is a sense of "unfinished business," an "it's-too-late" sensation, a frustrating emotion of futility, a dread of dependence, and a feeling of helplessness. These may be present in *every* unconscious at the involutional period, but only the immature and incompletely developed emotional mechanism will yield to them. The psychic reactions of the climacteric occur only when psychosexual development and adjustment have been faulty or incomplete.

Paranoid Reaction. This outward projection of unconscious frustration, insecurity, and deprivation may be expressed as bitterness—the individual is the victim of a "dirty deal"—the world is against him. Well-marked delusions of persecution are common. Such an individual is suspicious, withdraws from society, and drifts into the later years, a cantankerous, acrid, irritable, unloving, and unloved person.

Melancholia. The predominating features of this reaction are overwhelming sadness, agitation, tearfulness, death wishes, and, all too frequently, attempts at suicide. Such a patient, particularly as a reaction to unconscious guilt feelings, says he is unworthy, "no good," a "burden"; that he is responsible for all the misery in the world. This can progress to the point where, in a frank psychotic state, he feels that he is actually dead, or that everyone has died, leaving him as the sole survivor to suffer punishment for the sins of the entire universe. All involutionally depressed persons are positive that the future is gloomy and hopeless. Their constant attitude is one of utter futility. There is no reason to try to do anything to help themselves—there is no reason to live.

It is the person who unconsciously (and often consciously) dreads old age, loneliness, insecurity, who feels that the desire for love has been unrequited, or that he or she has failed to meet life's challenges when young, who is a candidate for psychic difficulties during the middle years.

TREATMENT OF MENTAL DISORDERS OF THE MIDDLE YEARS

One common misconception concerning therapy must be corrected before the subject can be pursued. Hormones are *not* the exclusive answer to the need for treatment in involutional disorders. True, estrogenic hormones help to assuage symptoms such as "hot flashes," sweats, tensions, uneasiness, and headaches. Otherwise, they are of little or no value in true involutional melancholia. There is only one instance in which a hormone, *chorionic testosterone,* is proving to be of material benefit. In the male who complains of sexual difficulties, such as poor erection, premature ejaculation, lack of control, etc., this hormonal agent often relieves these complaints.

The depressive state of the climacterical psychosis calls for close supervision or institutionalization because of the hazard of suicide. The general regimen of therapy is the same as in any deep, prolonged depression, i.e., tranquilization and electric shock therapy. The melancholic patient usually is malnourished, dehydrated, and emaciated because of a disinclination to eat and drink properly. A well-balanced diet, reinforced with vitamins and minerals, as well as physiotherapy, is indicated.

The paranoid type of involutional psychosis has a less favorable prognosis. Tranquilizers are used solely as an attempt to make the patient amenable to individual intensive psychotherapy. Other modalities of treatment are neither specific nor outstandingly successful. In these patients it is a common finding, after meticulous probing into the past life and careful study of a detailed history, that the prepsychotic personality reaction-type had *always* been paranoid, but that the fully overt manifestations (delusions of persecution, sarcastic denunciations, continual suspiciousness, etc.) did not become marked and noticeable until the advent of the climacteric. Such an individual prior to this period may have been episodically irritable and disagreeable, "a poor sport," "unreasonable," etc. To most psychiatrists these reactions imply, diagnostically, instances of superficially adjusted schizophrenics for whom the involution is the final trigger that explodes a dormant mental illness into full and open expression.

The neurotic whose emotional difficulties have been precipitated by the advent of the climacteric requires therapy in much the same manner as the individual suffering from a frank neurosis (see Chapter 6).

WIDOW, WIDOWER, AND DIVORCEE

A separate consideration of the widowed and divorced segments of our population is merited by a statistical peculiarity in this country. Of the more than ten millions of such persons, females outnumber males by better than eight to one! Without doubt, the high rate of coronary disease among men, particularly in the fifth and sixth decades, is the responsible factor for the one-sided survival ratio. Certainly, it is immediately obvious that, confronted with this lopsided mathematical disadvantage, over eight million widows and divorcees face a grim problem of readjustment.

Widows are younger today; the relict in her forties is an everyday finding. Mortality figures reveal that her husband probably died of heart disease (the cause of 52 per cent of all deaths in this country). Coronary afflictions rarely strike women. Moreover, they seem to have a predilection for the middle and upper economic and intellectual strata. No other professional group, for example, is devastated by coronary disease as much as physicians.

THE GENERAL PATTERN

For some time our civilization, has associated moral laxity and deviant behavior with the previously married female. She is "the gay divorcee" and "the merry widow" with all that these designations imply. To men, the widow is amenable to suggestion; to the smugly secure married woman, the relict is wanton. No matter how sedately she comports herself, the widow is followed in her community by raised eyebrows and knowing leers.

While every rule has its exception, the pattern of the forty- to fifty-five-year-old woman, following the death of her husband, is generally the same. Most widows, with rare exception, live a life, no matter how brief, that is a glaring contradiction of previous years. The most cultured and educated relict, the product of a well-adjusted childhood and home life, who has pursued a balanced mode of living, can turn out to be a carefree, excessively extraverted, fun-seeking woman, indulging in indiscriminate and foolhardy activities that are often incredible—incredible because we are inclined to equilibrate intellectual acumen with emotional maturity. She is a victim of self-deception, buoyed by the (necessary) belief that she has a perfect right to do as she pleases.

The one well-known exception to this pattern is the deeply religious female who emotionally wears her weeds forever, shunning all male companionship, quietly and genteelly mourning her loss and bearing her loneliness with quasi-stoicism. Many of these women suffer severe mental reactions precipitated by the climacteric, the harbinger of old age.

THE PROBLEM OF ADJUSTMENT

A certain number of widows have an item of "unfinished business" that must be completed before they feel free to plunge into the social whirl. If a relict has suffered an emotional trauma in her first marriage, no matter how trivial, her eye-for-an-eye unconscious demands equivalent, albeit symbolic, retribution. The unconscious does not function quantitatively or qualitatively. Once is the same as a thousandfold. Emotionally, an epithet, a slap, and actual infidelity are equivalent. Each implies rejection; each indicates that she is held by her mate as inferior, and expiation becomes mandatory. One example is cited to illustrate this point.

Mr. and Mrs. M. were regarded by friends as a perfectly happy couple, and so they were. One day Mrs. M. called for her husband at his office. While he was at a conference she began to idly inspect the well-appointed room. She admired the furniture, the thick carpet, and the fixtures. In a closet she discovered a small overnight bag. With typical feminine curiosity Mrs. M. opened it and found a shirt, shorts, socks, pajamas, toilet kit, and—a contraception apparatus. True, Mr. M. had not been caught *in flagrante delicto* but this sign of infidelity made a deep impression on his wife's unconscious mind. A few years later the lady became a widow and in eighteen months embarked on a round-the-world cruise. The second night at sea, under the magic spell of Pacific stars, soft music, and a few drinks, symbolically secluded from the world by Stygian darkness, the widow retired with a petty officer to his cabin. A few hours of acquaintanceship, a dance or two, a stroll around the deck—these were sufficient cause for an otherwise cultured and fastidious woman, reared by religious parents, a virgin at marriage and faithful to her wedding vows, to reject her own code of ethics. However, the score had to be evened, and was, subsequently, numerous times for good measure. With this belated triumph Mrs. M. had to inform the world of her victory and regained superiority. At the next port she dashed off dozens of letters to friends, describing her tropical nights in ill-disguised words. She told everyone. *Everyone, that is, except her two married daughters!*

In an attempt to readjust to "life on her own" the widow not infrequently becomes involved in difficulties resulting in psychic and/or somatic disasters. Too many relicts, trying to emulate the gay and vivacious teenager, and trying "to forget," fall prey to alcoholism, which Dr. Sidney Greenberg, eminent authority on the subject, terms the "disease of a million women." He points out that in the past twenty years the number of female alcoholics has doubled. Dr. Greenberg adds that many women, of whom widows and divorcees are not an inconsiderable number, drink "to release sexual frustrations or inhibitions" and "to (be) rid of fears, depressions, and 'evil thoughts.'"

The widower who was the "small boy dependent on his mother surrogate" may resort to liquor in his floundering for a prop. The widower who was unhappily married and is suddenly "emancipated" may go overboard and become an alcoholic.

In our civilization the widower's prime concern is not remarriage; he does not experience the "desperation" of the widow. In the phrenetic, odds-on competition for a companion and/or husband, with the not too unconscious feeling that she has lost her youthfulness and glamor, the female relict too often becomes reckless and indulges in a sexual relationship, not for pleasure *per se*, but "to prove she is a woman." Frequently, this leads to promiscuity that is not the indulgence of confident, capable women, but women who have been defeated. It does not attract women of achievement, but only those looking for achievement. Like a narcotic, promiscuity destroys a person, and a temporary blackout the night before merely postpones unsolved problems until the next day, with the person even less able to cope with them. Psychologically, the promiscuous widow is not oversexed at all—she is undersexed. She does not seek to give something, but to get it. She must realize that the act of love is outgoing; it can only be defiled, perhaps forever, by trying to make it a feminine accomplishment.

The widow who is not financially independent frequently faces difficulties in finding remunerative employment. If she has a profession—nursing or teaching, for example—she is reasonably assured of economic independence. Often she does very well as a receptionist or a librarian. Sometimes she is forced to accept more arduous work with insufficient return. Witness the number of widows behind department store counters. A widower has been accustomed to working, but a widow may not have earned a salary for years or at all. For this economic aspect alone she is more anxious to remarry than her male counterpart.

While the widower may seek female companionship soon after the death of his wife, generally it takes from fifteen to eighteen months for a widow's grief to fade sufficiently before she is ready to step out on her first date. The memory of her husband—what he was and what he meant to her—has slowly "blurred" into a mental image of what she would have liked him to have been, that is, what she now hopes to find. In a way, the mental paragon is a hindrance. Failing to discover the desired mate immediately, the widow, straining at the physiological leash and with time breathing down her neck, somewhat impetuously and carelessly grabs what comes her way and plunges into an affair without any prior assay of the situation.

There are several hazards facing all widows. The question of empty hours is perhaps the most immediate. Gainful and interesting employment goes far in filling the daytime. If there are children the widow is not alone, for they are living mementos of her married love. She can fill her evening with friends with whom she and her husband had socialized. Many widows hesitate to visit these friends, feeling out of place, "like a fifth wheel." There is no justification for this reaction. Understanding friends will often arrange dinners and evenings so that the relict may have male companionship. A widow can join civic movements, pursue cultural studies at night school and college, attend concerts and theaters. Nor must she follow these diversions alone. She can enjoy them with other widows just as happily as she plays bridge with them. This does not imply that the widow must forego dates with men, whether as a couple or with a group of couples. How much or how little sex is involved, if any, before a widow remarries (if she does) depends on her physiological demands, her self-confidence, and her moral standard.

The greatest threat to the widow's psychological well-being is the emotional havoc unconscious feelings of guilt may wreak, although successful sublimation can temporarily by-pass a sense of shame and self-reproach by quasi-righteousness. An example of the latter is the woman who claims "it is my business what I do," "there is nothing wrong with it," "plenty of others are no different," etc. Nevertheless, unconscious guilt invariably finds its way to the surface. Emotional reactions, psychosomatic conditions, neurosis, even frank psychosis, are potential end results.

SOCIAL ORGANIZATIONS

There are many organizations throughout the country maintained by widowers, widows, and divorcees for the ostensible purpose of providing a social milieu for the unattached middle-aged individual. These groups hold weekly or monthly dances and on the surface are means for club-like get-togethers. There is the strong hint that these meetings enhance the possibility of remarriage. This writer, who has interviewed many members of such clubs and attended their affairs, has never found one instance of marriage within *any* such social organization. All evidence indicates these clubs are simply associations for sublimated assignations and indiscriminate liaisons. Here conduct is oriented on primitive drives with almost complete disregard for early training and principles, in accordance with the theory of Konrad Lorenz, eminent naturalist, that "moral judgments are irrelevant where life is instinctive."

The group relict invariably claims she is hungry for companionship. This is the first prop for self-deception. The true companionship of man and woman—sharing confidences, joys, sorrows, mutual likes, on equal or nearly equal cultural and intellectual levels—is found in a lifetime union, not for a night or spasmodically for several months. Too often the author has found a widow who, although she is a college graduate and avidly interested in the arts, is having an affair with a widower whose education had been limited to grammar school and whose interests have centered on race tracks, fishing, and poker. However, he *is* after sex and finds a willing and co-operative partner in the club widow who does not wish to lose his attention.

It is a psychological truism that the well-adjusted husband and wife are prepared for the possibility that one of them may have to face the later years alone. The relict who has not been so fortified and consequently encounters emotional and psychic difficulties needs help. Temporizing spells disaster; nervously flitting from friend to friend or consulting untutored counselors can be harmful rather than beneficial. A troubled psyche calls for a skilled psychiatrist.

15: The Later Years

A few years ago an eminent American surgeon declared that "medical science was making it possible for man to live longer to suffer more complications." This statement, now an actuality, has created a paradox: the more that is done for one end of life's span (reduction of infant mortality), the greater are the problems at the other. At the turn of the present century, only 4 per cent of Americans were over sixty-five years of age. By 1975 this figure will have risen to 13 per cent of the population, or a total of twenty-five million individuals. The two factors principally responsible for the increased percentage are: decline in immigration and birth rates, and prevention and control of infectious diseases.

Just as it is not advisable to attempt to treat children as "younger adults," so it is unreasonable to try to treat persons over sixty-five as "older adults." Identical symptoms in an octogenarian and a man of thirty can be evidence of widely different conditions. Accordingly, the approach to afflictions in the aged is not the same as it is for younger individuals. For example, whereas dizziness is highly suggestive of hypertension (high blood pressure) in the elderly patient, in a young man it may indicate labyrinthine disease (a disorder of the delicate "balancing mechanism" in the inner ear) or irregularities of the heart. It was not until 1914 that the late Ignaz L. Rascher invented the term "geriatrics" for that branch of medicine dealing with the health problems of the aged. (The scientific body of knowledge pertaining to the process of aging is called "gerontology.") Rascher declared that medicine's challenge is to restore a diseased organ or tissue to a state that is normal in senility, *not* to a state that is normal in maturity. The Gerontological Society dedicates itself to the ideal: "to add life to years, rather than years to life."

THE AGING PROCESS

An understanding of the aging process as it relates to organs and tissues is essential to an appreciation of the mental and emotional problems of the later years of life because accumulated physical handicaps, plus a general deterioration in bodily functions, superimpose a heavier burden on whatever emotional traumata may have developed within the individual. The outstanding sign of aging is found in body tissues, where *stroma* (connective tissue, or nonfunctional elements) increases while *parenchyma* (functional tissue) decreases. Every organ of the body pursues its individual pattern of aging; only the blood remains essentially the same throughout all of life. The skin becomes thinner, drier, and darker; bones develop a brittle quality; muscles lose their power and decrease in magnitude; nerve cells vanish and nervous reactions become sluggish. Arterial vessels lose their elasticity and their ability to respond to metabolic demands for dilation and contraction. Sclerosis (hardening) of arterial walls converts soft vessels into "pipe stems," a condition which requires stronger cardiac action to overcome the added resistance to circulation. Thus, pulse rate and blood pressure rise. Heart muscle thickens, but the organ's efficiency diminishes as fat and fibrous tissue accumulate around it. The heart's control mechanism fails and irregularities of rate ensue, such as auricular fibrillation and premature contractions. The kidney loses many of its "units" (nephrons), while the remaining ones suffer deterioration.

The endocrine glands, particularly the thyroid, reveal changes as the years pass by. It is becoming clinically apparent that a decrease in hormones (the secretion of these glands), may be as important a factor in aging as a flagging vascular system. For example, sex hormones are directly involved in the organism's actions on proteins. The hormone "estrogen" is needed to metabolize fat, and when its secretion diminishes it is possible that cholesterol, in the form of animal fat, is then free to be deposited on vessel walls. It is alleged that this opens the road to arteriosclerosis. But there is the further question: is the diminution of sex hormones responsible for senility, or does it result from a failure of the pituitary to secrete its growth hormone?

When the latter has been injected into aged animals, some changes suggestive of youthfulness have resulted. A full understanding of this entire relationship between glands and aging is still awaiting experimental findings. Hormonal therapy tried with human beings has not produced uniform responses.

Research has tended to concentrate on the *cell* as the core of the problem of aging. We know that old cells have less water and more solids than younger ones. In the laboratory, test tube colloids lose water as they age. From this it has been argued that the aging of colloidal protoplasm accounts for the ravages of advanced years. In a similar manner, old cells accumulate pigments and lipids (fat substances) which many investigators maintain clog the cells and impair their efficiency. Other physiologists point to the reduction of cellular enzymes (chemical substances that break down matter in metabolism) as the answer, and many other cellular substances and activities are undergoing experimental scrutiny.

Aging affects the organism's response to stress; the reaction to injury is slower and less vigorous, and frequently less effective than in earlier years. Therefore, signs and symptoms of disease processes are often minimal because the signs and symptoms are generated by the response to injury and are very seldom due to injury itself. For example, widespread inflammation, muscular rigidity, cough, pain, and fever in the elderly may be minor to the point that an acute process such as pneumonia may not be suspected and the aged person thus delays seeking medical aid until it is too late. Senile persons do not bear extremes well—heat, cold, overeating, starvation, and dehydration. Even the heartiest old individual is at best only "comparatively" well; he has accumulated many scars from the hazards of life, such as injurious habits, poor nutrition, intoxications, infections, and actual injuries, not to mention the psychological traumata which are incident to a long life. Early years pave the way for later ones; the older one becomes, the more yesteryears are accumulated, and since life experiences differ in sequence, intensity, duration, and severity, a wide divergence and variation in functional capacities can be anticipated. The keynote, therefore, in geriatric medicine is *individualization*. Each elderly person must be separately assessed and inventoried. There is no such thing as "routine" therapy.

THE ROLE OF MENTAL DISORDER IN SENILITY

Mental disorders attributable to senility and arteriosclerosis create many of the handicaps of later life. It is incumbent on geriatric medicine to concern itself with (1) the fundamental nature of chronic diseases common to old age, and (2) the characteristics of the elderly and the process of aging.

The changes produced by old age are many: changes in emotional reactions, in intellectual functioning, response to stress, immunity, biochemical equilibrium, metabolism, and structure, to mention but a few. The advent of tranquilizing agents in psychiatric practice accounts for the decrease in institutional admission statistics, but this benefit has not accrued to the elder age bracket. The explanation is that the ataractics calm the disturbed, assuage anxiety, and relieve depressive reactions, but it is seldom that the senile or sclerotic patient is the "violent, unmanageable, intractable" individual. He has come to the hospital because his psychic-emotional apparatus has "run down" to the point where he is unable to remain in a competitive society. A clue to this situation is to be found in the language of therapy: whereas a cure is sought in mental disorders of young persons, in the elderly we hear the term "rehabilitation" constantly used. Thus, in 1930, only 5 per cent of all psychiatric admissions were over the age of sixty. These patients lived, after institutionalization, on the average, about two and one-half years. A quarter of a century later the admissions of patients over sixty had risen to slightly less than 40 per cent and they were surviving hospitalization for ten years.

Recognition of "abnormal" mental and emotional features in persons of advanced years remains one of the perplexities of medical practice. Considering the circumstances, how much irascibility, how much suspicion, how much "childishness" is justifiable in the reactions of the aged? Are disorientation, lack of defecatory control, intellectual letdown, etc., indications of mental disorder, or are they just the accompaniments of "simple" senility? Somewhat the same question exists with regard to pregnancy (surely this is not a "normal," uncomplicated state, but is it "abnormal"?). Is not the loss of physical vigor enough to sadden the best of men? Is the feeling of rejection and being shunned by relatives an inappropriate cause for an older person's sense of futility, hopelessness, and despair? When old age is a barrier to employment the job-hunter may well become paranoid and suspect that "the world is against him." Numerous such instances of social maladjustment are in the background of the mental disorders of the aged.

Beyond this, however, is a very real and pressing situation—the growing demand for centers, homes, or hospitals for the aged, the realization of which seems impossible because of the mounting tax burden.

The Principal Clinical Entities. In cerebral arteriosclerosis, the most common disorder of old age, symptoms and signs can be categorized as both physical and mental.

PHYSICAL SYMPTOMS. The patient may complain of headache, usually a throbbing pain, with or without "ringing in the ears." There may be dizziness, a feeling of pressure on or in the head, and fainting spells. The patient may suffer apoplectic strokes with or without paralysis. Examination of retinal vessels (in the back of the eye) via the ophthalmoscope will show arteriosclerotic changes. The pupil may have a white ring (*arcus senilis*, or the circle of old age). Blood pressure will be high if smaller vessels (arterioles) are thickened, but arteriosclerosis of large arteries may produce no elevation of pressure. The physical status of the heart will have a definite bearing on blood pressure.

MENTAL SYMPTOMS. The most striking indication of a mental change is "mental tension defect"—the impairment of the capacity to think readily and accurately, to concentrate and fix the attention. The patient is easily fatigued, emotionally, physically, and mentally. He shows a lack of emotional control—weeping over trivial events, or exhibiting irritability with explosive outbursts, especially as he reacts to the feeling that he is not as capable, physically and mentally, as he has been. Emotional disturbances may arise from arteriosclerotic involvement of the thalamus, that portion of the brain regarded as the seat of emotional control. The patient's memory is poor, presenting "patchy" defects, i.e., memory may be good one day and impaired the next. Realization that he is "under par" may cause the patient to be depressed and warrant close supervision to prevent self-destruction. In cases of impotence he may "project" his inadequacy and develop suspicions and paranoid ideas, accusing his wife of infidelity. Mental confusion in the sclerotic is episodic. These periods usually clear up, but each time the "return" is not as complete as the former period of recovery. This is called a "step letdown" defect that leaves the patient worse after each attack. He is prone to delirious attacks, especially at night, when he experiences terrifying hallucinations of death, burial, funerals, etc. The patient may cling to one expression, constantly repeating a previous thought or word (*perseveration*).

Obviously, an elderly individual may react to *both* arteriosclerosis and senility. However, when a patient has one syndrome exclusively, a differential diagnosis is possible, as follows:

CEREBRAL ARTERIOSCLEROSIS	SENILITY
Occurs early in old age.	Seen in the later years.
Of brief duration.	Slightly longer duration.
The onset is apt to be abrupt and stormy.	The onset is gradual.
Intellect confused.	Intellect normal.
Depressive and hypochondriacal states are common.	Depressive and hypochondriacal states are unusual.
Paranoid states are present but not marked.	Paranoid states are very common.
Headaches, dizziness, stroke, fainting, convulsions are present.	These symptoms are rare.
Capricious defects of memory: "patchy."	Orderly, retrograde defect of memory.
Blood pressure may be elevated.	Blood pressure not elevated *per se.*
Personality is fairly well preserved.	Personality is not well preserved.

THE OBJECTIVE: CONTROL RATHER THAN CURE

Nowhere in the field of psychiatry is the holistic principle more meaningful than in geriatrics. The aged person's mental condition will always be complicated by organic disorders of some kind. Old persons are immune to no disease; they even lose immunity to childhood diseases. However, the major problem is that of chronic, "degenerative" diseases which include gout, arthritis, arteriosclerosis, high blood pressure, inadequate or poorly functioning metabolism, and nutritional disorders such as diabetes, anemia, and gonadal deficiency. Most of the disorders of old age are of doubtful etiology, arising usually from factors within the patient, highly variable, and in operation years before they are overtly manifested. Perhaps, if the average person underwent regular and routine physical examination, medicine would have a better idea, for example, of the causes of high blood pressure, the victim of which commonly consults a physician only after he has suffered for years. However, unless and until the causes are established, geriatric medicine must aim at control rather than cure and at prevention through better supervision and living. Pernicious anemia can be controlled by the administration of liver, and diabetes by insulin and diet; but they are not "cured." This is not unusual in any sphere of medicine, but it is perhaps more applicable to conditions of the aged. Geriatric medicine aims, consequently, to widen the breach between disease and disability or death.

LONGEVITY

Longevity is a subject that has interested man since pre-Biblical times and has resulted in considerable scientific investigation together with many myths, metaphysical tracts, amazing anomalies, and questionable statistics. The subject commands the attention of health agencies, welfare groups, sociologists, underwriters, and, of course, legislators and social reformers. Raymond Pearl, a leading geneticist, showed that in fruit flies long-livedness is a dominant factor while short-livedness is recessive. No one, however, has proved how this genetic mechanism actually works. Hygienic and medical progress, both for the individual and the group, have served, particularly in recent times, to prolong man's life expectancy. In the Caesarian era the average length of life was twenty-three years; in 1900 this had increased to forty-six and in 1950 to sixty-nine. In other words, it took two thousand years to double life expectancy but only fifty additional years to triple it! Scientists have shown that natural selection and fortuitous combinations of chromosomes and genes account for long-livedness, yet a physicochemical explanation maintains that it is not the duration of life as such that is hereditarily determined, but only longevity in the sense of a definite quanity of life energy. Length of life may be affected by metabolic acceleration or retardation, influenced by agents such as temperature and light, which control the rate of consumption of the fixed available supply of energy. It is statistically known that thin persons generally live longer than fat people; women outlive men; and in the young, a higher mortality rate prevails among those of below average height.

When occupational and socioeconomic features are considered, statistics are frequently blurred by legendary and uncorroborated reports. Well-known examples are the Biblical accounts of the incredible limits of age reached by Isaac and Methuselah. It seems that intellectual pursuits favorably influence longevity: in science and literature there are Isaac Newton, Bernard de Fontenelle, Johann Wolfgang von Goethe, Georges de Buffon, and Immanuel Kant; in art, Michelangelo and Titian; in medicine, William Williams Keen, Georges Duvernoy, Hans Sloane, and William Harvey. Samuel Hahnemann married at eighty and was hard at work eight years later; Izaak Walton was busy writing at ninety; Mary Somerville penned her *Molecular and Microscopic Science* at eighty-six; and Walter Savage Landor dashed off his *Imaginary Conversations* when eighty-five. In contemporary times noted octogenarians have included Nicholas Murray Butler and Justice Oliver Wendell Holmes. History provides innumerable examples of men and women who were mentally active and vigorous in the senium: William R. Hearst, Thomas A. Edison, Henry Ford, John D. Rockefeller, Pius XII, Gustavus V, Winston Churchill, Bernard Baruch, Queen Victoria, Otto von Bismarck, William E. Gladstone, Ferdinand de Lesseps, and Michel Chevreul. On his hundredth birthday, Sir Moses Montefiore was at his desk!

Concerning longevity records, the case of Henry Jenkins is the most amazing. He was born in Yorkshire, England, in 1501 and died in 1670. There is a record in the office of the King's Remembrancer that he appeared as a witness at the age of one hundred and fifty-seven. Peter Garden of Auchterless, who died at the age of one hundred and thirty-one years in 1755, had chatted with Jenkins about the battle of Flodden Field which Henry had beheld as a boy of twelve. Thus, Mr. Garden could tell the tale of a battle which had taken place two hundred and sixty-two years before, from a description furnished him by an actual eyewitness!

Another notable record was established by the Horrocks family in England. James Horrocks was born in 1744 and lived to celebrate his hundredth birthday. His father had been born in 1657. James was the son of a second marriage when the elder Horrocks was eighty-seven. Therefore, this man could truly declare in 1844 that he had a brother born when Charles II was king, and that his father was a citizen of the Commonwealth. Another and well-authenticated record is that of Dr. William Hotchkiss, born in 1755, who died on April 1, 1895! Similar cases continue to stir attention—some well-founded, others of dubious origin.

According to the 1950 census, there are about four thousand, five hundred centenarians in the United States. In 1958 two Confederate veterans, aged one hundred and twelve, and one hundred and fourteen, were granted Federal pensions. There are sixty-one persons past the hundred-year mark on the benefit rolls of the Social Security Office. Javier Pereira, a Colombian Indian who died in 1958, stating he was one hundred and sixty-eight years old, had been brought to the New York Hospital-Cornell Medical Center for purposes of examination. The physicians who completed this study declared Pereira might well have been over the age of one hundred and fifty at that time.

THE SOCIOECONOMIC FACTOR

The attitude of our civilization toward old age is a puzzling paradox. The elderly themselves are concerned with maintenance of social adjustments, of income, and of health. Despite alleged public interest in the problems of old age, leaders in politics, industry, sociology, and economics all seem bent on doing everything possible to make financial, social, and health adjustments unattainable for the aged. The longer man lives, the earlier becomes the age for retirement and/or pension. An unemployed man of fifty is regarded as "too old" in industry; the cry is for youth. In the nineteenth century the average American worked until he died. Perhaps this somewhat primitive "survival of the fittest" was not wholesome, but in spite of the alleged advantages of modern social privileges, programs such as social security, old age pensions, and unemployment insurance do not help aged individuals psychologically. They create a sense of futility in the aged, a feeling of dependence and uselessness. Children who, fifty years ago, would have regarded the care and responsibility of their aged parents and relatives as a moral requisite, now resent the presence of an old person in the house and anxiously seek a private nursing home or welfare establishment. They are intolerant of the feeble grandfather whose trembling hand spills soup on the table.

In an age of technology the United States is losing many fine skilled workers and alert, capable scientists through compulsory retirement. According to an insurance source, researchers examined the records of four hundred famous men, each the most outstanding writer, poet, soldier, artist, or statesman of his era, and found that 35 per cent of them recorded notable achievement when they were between sixty and seventy years old, 23 per cent between seventy and eighty, and 8 per cent after the age of eighty. In other words, 66 per cent of the world's greatest work has been accomplished by men past sixty!

Those over sixty-five years of age require the chance to work and to live comfortably because social security and pension programs are of themselves inadequate (and, if made adequate, could not be supported). There is a need for developing criteria for measuring the continued capacity to work. In the field of health there is a demand for research to determine which bodily alterations "must" be accepted as part of the normal aging process and which can be prevented or eliminated. Rehabilitation attempts and programs of centers and hospitals meet with little success because the elderly patient has little to anticipate once he is released. It is next to impossible for him to find employment, to maintain a self-respecting standard of living, and to anticipate love, sympathy, and respect from relatives and friends. Furthermore, too often do psychiatrists find that mental symptoms, particularly feelings of depression and futility, are not actual psychic indicators, but products of social and familial rejection. Without doubt, much of what is described as "senile decline" is due to lack of motivation rather than to the deterioration of old age. The senile individual, in addition, has further taxation on his social and mental adaptive processes: loss of self-respect, a feeling of being unwanted and unloved, changes in the environment, the death of dear ones, and enforced retirement. Since the adaptive mechanisms are not up to the task, the elderly person simply repeats ineffectual behavior or withdraws from the unfriendly world of reality. That this is a sheer waste of talent is borne out by the fact that through the use of batteries of tests psychologists have proved conclusively that reasoning, general information, knowledge, and vocabulary are preserved for longer periods than is commonly suspected. There is an urgent need for community services, such as counseling for the group and the individual, vocational placement and guidance, suitable housing, and recreational outlets.

The physician, too, must broaden his interest in the problems of old age and aging. He cannot confine himself solely to clinical matters, research, and treatment, but must regard the challenge as a total one that includes social and economic aspects as well. The true geriatrician cannot exclude environmental factors from his study of the patient. If the treatment program does not embrace the old person's psychosociological responses so that every aspect of his difficulties can be coped with, failure will result from emphasizing the incapacities caused by senility rather than stressing the patient's assets. In the words of Dr. R. H. Young: "it is imperative to appreciate . . . the geriatric patient as an individual with as many, or more, social and economic problems than medical."

Only one who is elderly can truly appreciate the psychological impact of later years. Bernard Baruch, approaching his ninetieth year, said: "We must get away from employment policies based on cold arithmetical averages and take advantage of the skills and judgments of older people. How hideous a mockery it would be if, as a result of advances in medicine, surgery, hygiene, and higher living standards, older people were kept willing and able to work—but society deprived them of something useful to do."

16: Love—A Basic Need

Whether in the limited sense of the sex act or in the lofty sense of reverence for a Supreme Being, the human phenomenon called "love" has captured the imagination of poets, philosophers, moralists, and even scientists from time immemorial. The concept of love has been oversweetened by advice-to-the-lovelorn columnists and soured by cynical essayists. Perhaps more than any other word in our language, "love" has suffered from misuse, as in such ridiculous phrases as "I *love* strawberries" and "Don't you just *love* Brahms?" Principally, though, it suffers from a multiplicity of meanings: sexual excitation and copulation, the mating experience, the total relationship between husband and wife, the feeling of parent for child and child for parent, sibling and other family relations, love of one's neighbor or fellow man (so-called "brotherly love"), and love of God—although these do not exhaust the list.

The English language is noted for its ambiguities and there is often confusion between the original meaning of a term and its popular connotation. In psychiatric usage, love is ordinarily associated with heterosexual adjustment, since this usually signifies that the individual has reached maturity. There can be little argument against the thesis that it should be the goal of every individual to progress through several preparatory stages (the autoerotic, narcissistic, and the homoerotic) to the mature state in which he or she finds a mate with whom physical, emotional, and intellectual satisfaction can be achieved and with whom children can be raised, cared for, and, in their turn, also guided to maturity. Oversimplified or platitudinous as it may sound, this is the ideal pattern of a human life.

Maturity or heterosexual adjustment is not, however, achieved without overcoming several hurdles. First, there is the need to pass the normal stages of development successfully. Next, there is the ever present factor of the biological and intellectual differences among individuals. Last, one must cope with the infinite variety of environmental experiences, which individuals interpret and react to in so many different ways. Just how many people ever do achieve complete maturity is open to question. To have married and raised a family is not necessarily proof that one has divested oneself of all the elements of the pre-mature personality. Nor has it been shown that unmarried or childless individuals contribute more than their share of psychiatric problems. Nevertheless, the attainment of a stable life, with established home and family, is a goal to be sought; the personality shows the fullest development when the individual has achieved this ideal, assuming of course that he or she is emotionally and otherwise well adjusted.

AN HISTORICAL REVIEW OF LOVE

Just as "the course of true love never did run smooth" in the individual case, neither has the role of love in the social structure remained constant through the ages. Ours is not the first era to regard love with cynicism, nor are the saccharine approaches of the nineteenth century the first such recorded in literature. At some risk of generalization, one can count off certain historical intervals and characterize them on the basis of the contemporary attitudes toward love.

Thirty centuries ago a lovesick Egyptian poet bemoaned an "illness" no doctor could cure but which yielded to his sweetheart's embraces. Marital bliss—and discord—were lampooned in the early Greek comedies but were given more significance in the Bible with the story of Adam and Eve. One of the oldest and most beautiful love stories is that of Rachel and Jacob, recorded in Genesis: ". . . and Jacob served seven years for Rachel; and they seemed unto him but a few days, for the love he had to her." Ancient history and literature contain many tales of supreme sacrifice to preserve marital love, such as the story of Orpheus who descended into Hades to regain his wife, Eurydice.

On the other hand, there are accounts of philandering—the wife who leaves her husband for a lover or the husband who deceives his wife. Helen of Troy's elopement with Paris was the direct cause of the Trojan War (yet afterwards she was received at home again by her spouse, Menelaus!). The first wife who we know was unfaithful while her mate was "away on business" was Clytemnestra. Ulysses engaged in several romantic interludes on his adventurous voyage home, while Penelope, the classical picture of the patient wife, repulsed all suitors.

The so-called "double standard" was popularized when, in the time of Socrates, women were supposed to be faithful while their husbands supported concubines, the original "kept women." When Plato wrote of the lofty love between human beings, regardless of sex, founded on a timeless love of Good and Beauty, he brought us the expression "platonic love." Christianity introduced into the picture a paradoxical concept that was both a boon and a curse, accounting in no small measure for contemporary confusion. While religious doctrine made the first attempt to unfetter women by preaching equality between the sexes, it also introduced the concept of sin into love; thus, love could be both profane and sacred.

In the Middle Ages, this concept was reflected in two diverse pictures presented by the literature. On the one hand, a knight was a personification of the romantic ideal, dedicated to the protection of the weak and all women. An individual knight sought the hand of a young, unmarried girl or bound himself hopelessly in service to another man's wife. Women were pedestaled in verse and song, yet the concept of love included cohabitation, although each such love usually ended tragically as in the case of Launcelot and Guinevere, Tristan and Isolde.

The Renaissance brought an open element of sensuality to love. Chivalry was ignominiously slain by Cervantes' tongue-in-cheek mockery. Somewhat later the French wallowed in an abundance of flowery prose and poetry in an over-sentimental approach to the subject. A certain amount of cynicism carried over, however, and French literature included derision for the husband unaware of his wife's infidelity. Shakespeare and Molière endowed literature with the term "cuckold."

England's Puritan Protestants emphasized the danger of sin attached to love with all the implications of eternal damnation and endless suffering for the unrepentant. This concept migrated to the American colonies and found expression in early colonial literature, particularly in Nathaniel Hawthorne's *The Scarlet Letter*.

Early in the eighteenth century the melancholic aspect of love was virtually laughed out of existence. People pursued *affaires du coeur* openly with no thought for moral obligations. Don Juan and Casanova were models for young men to emulate and types young women secretly desired. The role of woman had changed; no longer a symbol of love, she became primarily a means for pleasure.

The nineteenth century saw three distinct attitudes toward love. The early part of the century was the period of the great Romantic movement, when Shelley, Wordsworth, and Keats were the prominent figures and lyric poetry the dominating form in literature. The ideal of love and beauty which had been woven from the time of Plato and before reappeared again with the same strength it had shown during the Middle Ages. A stronger movement than the earlier French attempt, the Romantic period in England also incorporated something of the earlier styles; the satire of the Neo-Platonists found expression in such works as Byron's *Don Juan* and *English Bards and Scotch Reviewers*. The magnificence of medieval tradition was replaced by exotic Eastern influences and religious symbolism, outstanding examples of which can be seen in the works of Coleridge.

The Victorian era which followed had a restraining influence on the imagination of its writers. Sentimentality returned but was channeled toward an ideal of good men and good women, and the social scene gained prominence as a literary background. Despite the *rigeur* of Victorian comportment, in the latter part of the century there were the Oscar Wildes, the translations of the *Rubáiyát* of Omar Khayyám, and the unadulterated sensuality of the *Indian Love Lyrics* proclaiming:

> "For this is wisdom; to love, to live,
> To take what Fate, or the gods, may give,
> To ask no question, to make no prayer,
> To kiss the lips and caress the hair,
> Speed passion's ebb as you greet its flow—
> To have—to hold—and—in time—let go!"

The candy coating around love was swiftly and finally eradicated with the advent of World War I. Poetry, prose, and song emphasized realism; idealism and romanticism became associated with the past. Thus, we had John Held and F. Scott Fitzgerald, followed by John Steinbeck, Tennessee Williams, and Arthur Miller.

CONTEMPORARY ATTITUDES

Today the concept of love may be estimated as somewhere between sentiment and sex without inhibitions or excessive restrictions. Yet what is alleged to be liberal thinking and unrestrained discussion on the one hand is accompanied by a general lowering of moral attitude on the other. We are plagued by a record-breaking divorce rate. Writers reap fortunes through articles which give pseudo-solutions to sexual problems in marriage but which are predominately expositions on how to enjoy sex—read by young and old, married and unmarried. Sex is too frequently set apart from love in so-called "frank" plays and movies, lewd literature, and loose talk. There is emotional satisfaction and benefit from frank discussion, but there is irrefutable harm when frankness is a veneer for arousing unnatural curiosity, temptation, and crime through unscrupulous bypassing of social decency, such as is presented to all ages via the printed word, stage, screen, radio, and television. According to police statistics, prostitution flourishes as never before. Out of indiscriminate sexual activity by adolescents, by their philandering parents (married, divorced, or widowed), and by other adults, mental and emotional reactions —outgrowths of insecurity and guilt—have developed.

The present perplexity about love has received additional impetus from the insecurity of modern life and, to some degree, from the misrepresentation of and failure to comprehend the philosophy and dynamic approach of such investigators as Sigmund Freud. Endocrinology has revived the Ponce de Leon interest in sexual restoratives and encouraged manufacturers of nostrums to give false hope to the ever increasing army of impotent oldsters. Religion battles birth-control agencies on the issue of contraception. Drug stores sell pregnancy-thwarting devices to teen agers; gynecologists prescribe diaphragms and sperm-killing jelly for their unmarried female patients. Abortionists, lay and medical, do a land office business. In some states adultery is a statutory crime. While the street walker is subject to arrest, the economically independent woman who uses her body to assure herself of male companionship is not a prostitute —she is merely lonely.

PSYCHIATRIC CONSIDERATIONS OF LOVE

The most sensible approach to a consideration of love comes to us from the gifted pen of Dr. Félix Martí-Ibáñez, probably the ablest editorialist in the medical profession:

"Stendhal evolved the 'crystallization' theory in love: the sedimentation on one person of imaginary perfections projected by another. Just as a twig cast into the Salzburg salt mines, he said, is slowly coated by a myriad tiny iridescent salt crystals until transfigured into a glimmering wand of silver, so is the loved one transfigured into a vision of graces by the lover's imagination.

"Stendahl was wrong. True love is born suddenly and lasts forever. It is a motion of the soul towards something incomparable. To be in love is to feel bewitched by someone who is or seems perfect. Love first starts with a centripetal stimulus aroused by another person, which when it finally strikes the core makes love blossom centrifugally until it becomes a psychic current flowing endlessly towards that person.

"We all carry deep within us [in the unconscious] a preformed imaginary profile of the beloved that we try on most persons we meet. Therefrom springs the arrow, the French *coup de foudre* . . . love at first sight, when we suddenly meet someone who fits this ideal model.

"Although love is a dynamic feeling, it narrows our world; it is a psychic angina that begins with a change in our attention, which becomes obsessively fixed on one person. The image of the beloved fills our world completely. Hence, we do not 'crystallize' on the object of our love, but set it apart and stand hypnotized before it as a lion before a lion tamer. [This, in Freudian parlance, would be the supreme ego-ideal.] A lover's soul, filled with one single image, is like a sick man's room filled with the smell of flowers. In this sense, love impoverishes 'horizontally' our world, while enriching it 'vertically' with knowledge of another human being.

"Love, however, is not the same as sexual instinct. Whereas

love is born from another being whose qualities trigger the erotic process, sexual instinct pre-exists the object of desire, cares not for perfection, and insures only the continuation of the species, not its improvement. *Sexual instinct is sometimes selective; love is always so* [italics ours] and excludes all desired objects but *the* one. There is no love without the sexual instinct, but in true love such instinct merely serves the same purpose as the wind in sailing.

"Love, Ortega y Gasset said, is 'surrender by bewitchment,' not a will to surrender, but surrender despite oneself; one is engulfed as if by magic by the beloved. This is not so of desire, which entails no surrender, only the capture of the quarry. In desire the object of desire is absorbed; in love the lovesick one is absorbed. We can desire without loving, but we cannot love without desiring. Desire dies with fulfillment; love is never fully satisfied. Thus, love is the most delicate reflection of a person's soul, a wondrous talent granted to only a few." *

With each succeeding generation taking an about-face attitude toward the meaning of love, there can be no surprise that our present civilization is the neurotic child, the product of an emotionally insecure background. Psychiatrists are defied to produce a definition of love. That challenge will never be met. Search though you may through endless library shelves of standard psychiatric texts and tracts dealing with marriage, the term love is neither defined nor indexed!

Stendhal attempted, over a century ago, to specify four varieties of love: passion-love, sympathy-love, sensual-love, and vanity-love. The first is valid but the idea of "crystallization," described above, falls short of serving either as a definition or an explanation. All forms of love, however, have certain features in common. In heterosexuality it is an extraverted drive (as opposed to self-love or autoeroticism). Love must be reciprocated to be fully gratified; unrequited affection spells frustration. Love is individually selective in the higher forms of life; it arouses the impulse to give which supersedes but does not necessarily eliminate the desire "to take." It stimulates curiosity for the love object —both psychological and physical. Certainly sexual contact is a natural corollary of love, but it follows, it does not precede or

* Félix Martí-Ibáñez, "De l'Amour" (editorial), *MD, The Medical News-magazine*, 2:11 (April, 1958).

immediately accompany it. This statement at once provokes the question: can not clandestine, illicit love precede a full love life? It can, but the true and maximum appreciation of the emotion cannot be achieved while a sense of guilt, unconscious and/or conscious, detracts from the complete libidinal concentration on love. This guilt is the result of the illicit lovers ignoring their superego's complaints, the heritage of family, the dictates of society, of religion, etc.

Love, as we have presented it, exists in persons before the desire to have sexual intercourse. Thus, true lovers become more and more inseparable as they continue to learn each other's assets and liabilities. A couple genuinely in love may initially experience sexual difficulties. Were they not in love, these handicaps would be seized as an excuse and magnified until they were accepted as a reason for dissolving the union. To the contrary, under the revealing light of love, two people can frankly, co-operatively, and successfully overcome these difficulties. The emotionally mature woman, for example, who marries for love will experience thoroughly satisfying sex. The emotionally immature woman who goes from one liaison to another solely for physiological gratification thereby prostitutes herself in the search for male companionship.

A SANE "SLANT" ON SEX

Says Dr. A. H. Maslow of Brandeis University: "One of the deepest satisfactions coming from the healthy love relationship reported by my subjects is that such a relationship permits the greatest spontaneity, the greatest naturalness, the greatest dropping of defenses and protection against threat. In such a relationship it is not necessary to be guarded, to conceal, to try to impress, to feel tense, to watch one's words or actions, to suppress or repress. My people report that they can be themselves without feeling that there are demands or expectations upon them; they can feel psychologically (as well as physically) naked and still feel loved and wanted and secure." *

At the outset of this chapter we synonymized love and heterosexual adjustment. The healthy attainment of mature love is

---

* A. H. Maslow, *Motivation and Personality* (New York: Harper & Bros., 1954), pp. 239–240.

another way of saying achievement of good mental hygiene. If we subscribe to the tenet of prevention rather than cure, then the proper point to launch a program of mental hygiene is at the beginning—when life commences. No one, regardless of age, is ever so richly endowed, intellectually and emotionally, that nothing remains to be learned. Instruction and guidance are of the utmost importance before puberty. Reaction patterns, personality traits, interpersonal relationships—these are in the making from the first breath of life.

Sex is more than the physiological satisfaction of desire. It is an important component and offshoot of love; it also implies the need to adjust, after psychosexual development has been completed, to a universe of man and woman. Parents, therefore, have an obligation beyond providing the necessities for existence. If they feel that anything more than this can be purchased or is guaranteed by law through payment of taxes, then they fail in their responsibility to their families. The teacher and the chaplain are important influences in a child's development. However, they cannot do the entire job without parental cooperation—any more than the nursemaid, baby sitter, grandparents, or television can be expected to serve as surrogates for mothers and fathers.

First and foremost the child should be given every reason to feel secure and wanted in the home. Honesty is the keystone in the arch of family love. Every minute brings a youngster something new that he wants to learn about; he will ask questions. If he is impatiently brushed aside—rejected—if the reply is untrue or veiled with mystery so as to connote wickedness or fear, not only do doubt and insecurity result, but confidence in the parent is shaken. If conversation threatens to turn to delicate topics, changing the subject is far better than the forefinger on the lips, the wink, the warning glare, or the foreign phrase that cautions the speaker. If you cannot answer a child's question because you lack the knowledge, say so, but then seek the information with the child. He will respect your honesty and when you do have the data to satisfy his queries he will believe you unconditionally.

Sex instruction deserves priority in child training. Properly administered and maturely handled, this feature of a youngster's bringing up will go far in molding a good citizen with healthy interests. All sex knowledge is not imparted to a child at any one age, any more than Euclid is taught before the student masters basic arithmetic. Simpler facts are explained at first, such as the age-old question, "where do babies come from?" As times goes on and the child's mind develops, further instruction is given. There is no need to dread this responsibility which, in fact, is a happy experience for both teacher and pupil. Brochures, pamphlets, and books are available in public libraries, from the American Medical Association, local mental health societies, and other agencies.

No household has to be a citadel of unnatural prudery. Neither should it be a center for vulgarity or off-color stories. A healthy, sincere, modern attitude of respect for sex, ever properly linking it to genuine love, will go far in advancing good mental hygiene. Such a home never has to worry when the teen-age daughter begins to date, or when the boy's voice changes and his chin sprouts a stubble. Sensible parents, earnest and moderate in attitude, fostering an atmosphere of family togetherness, will raise children who find complete satisfaction in scouting, hobbies, and athletics, and who will be untempted by narcotics, liquor, zip guns, and clandestinely pursued sensuality.

Sex should be neither emphasized nor ignored as a component of love. It is important to know the limitations of sexual attraction and to be able to distinguish it from real love; it should be a part but not a whole. George Santayana expresses the philosophic viewpoint in *The Life of Reason.* "There can be no philosophic interest in disguising the animal basis of love, or in denying its spiritual sublimations, since all life is animal in its origin and all spiritual in its possible fruits."

Finally, an excellent literary appreciation of love is given us by Thornton Wilder in *The Bridge of San Luis Rey.* ". . . we ourselves shall be loved for a while and forgotten. But the love will have been enough; all those impulses of love return to the love that made them. Every memory is not necessary for love. There is a land of the living and a land of the dead and the bridge is love, the only survival, the only meaning."

17: Religion and Psychiatry

Not until the second half of the twentieth century was a tenable and working understanding reached between religion and psychiatry. Even today many lay and professional people, continue to believe that no common meeting ground exists on which mental hygiene and theology can stand together with any degree of mutual confidence. One still hears such derogations as "psychiatry is anti-God," "the Church rejects and condemns psychoanalysis," and, on the other hand, "religion is a man-made gimmick born of ancient superstition and therefore emotionally unacceptable to the instinctual unconscious."

RELIGION AND SCIENCE

The history of the relationship between religion and science has not been a happy one. While many of the advances in our knowledge of the workings of nature have been achieved through the sponsorship of religious bodies (the early universities were Church-controlled), they have just as often been retarded by these same bodies. A heavy burden of mythology, astrology, theology, and priestcraft pervaded the writings of the classical Greek investigators of nature. In the modern era, James Harvey, in the Preface to his immortal treatise on the circulation of the blood, felt obliged to pay tribute to prevailing clerical dogma, as did most of his colleagues (this gesture was a sort of apologetic for disagreeing with their "elders"). Discussions of the causes of commonplace phenomena frequently degenerated into heated debates over theories which clashed with established ecclesiastical dogma.

Resistance to change is not, however, confined to theologians. Men do not easily surrender concepts which they have originated or accepted, whether in the field of culture, economics, or medicine. The fearsome hand of Galen (who died in A.D. 200) restrained the development of medicine for centuries, for his observations, which were hopelessly beclouded by mysticism, obscurities, and downright error, were swallowed whole by many investigators who followed him, even until the eighteenth century. Although Anton von Leeuwenhoek demonstrated the existence of bacteria in 1683, and others supported his views in the interim, it was not until late in the nineteenth century, thanks to Schwann, Pasteur, and some others, that the idea that disease could be caused by microorganisms was generally accepted. Even in the twentieth century, the medical profession has been reluctant to give serious consideration to the influence of purely psychic factors in disease.

It must be admitted, nevertheless, that medical science and theology have both come a long way in their study of man. Neither has evolved the "final answers" to man's role in the universe, but to their credit they are striving harder than ever before to humanize their approach to his psychic (or spiritual) and physical problems. Each has moved a bit in the direction of the other. By its increasing recognition of the psychosomatic concept, medicine has abandoned to some degree its "ivory tower" view that the only factors in illness that are worth consideration are those that can be demonstrated in the laboratory. Conversely, theologians, in pastoral writings and through the creation of seminars in psychiatry for the clergy and clergy-in-training, have conceded that physiologic function can play a significant role in disturbances of thought.

Lest the reader should too readily dismiss religion as "contrary to science," the words of Albert Einstein are offered to him:

"The most beautiful experience we can have is the mysterious. It is the fundamental emotion which stands at the cradle of true art and true science. Whoever does not know it and can no longer wonder, no longer marvel, is as good as dead, and his eyes are dimmed. It was the experience of mystery—even if mixed with fear—that engendered religion. A knowledge of the existence of something we cannot penetrate, our perceptions of the profoundest reason and the most radiant beauty, which only in their most primitive forms are accessible to our minds—it is this knowledge and this emotion that constitute true religiosity." *

PSYCHOLOGICAL ASPECTS OF RELIGION

There is ample evidence for the hypothesis that religion is as much an integral part of the instinctual element of man's personality as are hunger and sex. With all his pride in having mastered the forces of nature and put them to use, man is still baffled by a number of mysteries concerning the universe and life, in both the physical and the philosophic sense. There remain such imponderables as the Creation (of which there are countless versions in the world's many faiths); teleological questions, or curiosity over purpose in nature; the existence of a Supreme Being, who is blamed for practically everything that happens (or does not happen) to people either in general or as individuals (often as an escape from personal responsibility); and the wonderment over whether, when, and how "it" will all end. These are the principal considerations that cause man to feel his limitations and turn to spiritual guidance for reasurance, i.e., to nullify feelings of insecurity.

The man who senses uncertainty and turns to a Superior Force for leadership and assistance is the parallel of the child who relies on his father. It was Carl Jung who recognized the importance of this relationship when he evolved his concept of the unconscious as consisting of two portions: the *personal* unconscious (the ontogenetic element) and the *racial* or *collective* unconscious (the phylogenetic element). With regard to the latter, Jung pointed out how man's heritage, down through the ages, has endowed his personality, unconsciously, with drives and impulses, many of which are directly derived from beliefs overtly followed by his ancestors and which, by rote, gradually sank from the conscious mind into the unconscious. As explained earlier, this pattern is the duplicate of that whereby a baby learns personal hygiene and toilet habits "consciously" and through constant repetition, so that what is taught becomes "automatic" and "unconsciously" pursued.

* Albert Einstein, *Ideas and Opinions* (New York: Crown Publishers, Inc., 1954), p. 11.

In keeping with this thought, it can be appreciated that religions grow from and take on the character of the cultures in which they originate. With the waning of animism and polytheism in the face of rising monotheism, the family became the basic unit for religious systems. Because the majority of the peoples of the earth live under patriarchal rather than matriarchal organizations, it has naturally followed that the Supreme One or the spiritual leader has been referred to as Father or some equivalent title. Thus, we have Pope, padre, Master, etc.

It cannot be denied that respect for the head of the household (who is at the same time the protector of those in his family group) is a most desirable feature of any culture and that, in encouraging this, religion affords the most fertile soil for the cultivation of wholesome social and personal attitudes. Indeed, this is one of the common grounds on which psychiatry and religion are beginning to approximate one another, for clinical experience shows that disintegration of the family or weakening of rapport among its members is a prime factor in the development of mental disorders.

Another area for co-operation between psychiatry and religion touches upon one of the basic Freudian concepts of personality development. This concerns the formation of the *ego ideal*. As the child grows he gradually acquires an image of himself as an individual. To form this image he borrows mainly from the people around him. Parents, relatives, teachers, and others who cross his path play a role as their influence is brought to bear in varied circumstances. The child is continually making comparisons, accepting certain qualities and rejecting others. If he habitually encounters drunken, sadistic, or unsympathetic people, there is some risk that he may incorporate their characteristics into his ego ideal. The introduction of religious concepts into his sphere of learning serves the purpose of directing the image of the kind of person he wants to become into desirable channels. It gives him, in an impressive way, the appreciation of an authority which is analagous to, but transcends, parental control. There is, of course, the danger that the individual will assume that religion is an end in itself and, failing to grasp the analogy, will treat it as little more than an instrument for obtaining favors from the Almighty. Still, the loftier precepts are available to him; how he will use them will depend on his intellectual and emotional constitution and his life experiences.

The ritualistic aspects of religion have unquestionable therapeutic value. Flickering candles, stirring music, a robed choir, and the very architecture of the house of worship tend to induce sober reflection and respect for the better side of life. The depressed may find solace, the agitated may be calmed, the antisocial may come to appreciate the need to live in peace and harmony with their fellow men. Even the atheist must agree that, by and large, people are at their best when they are at worship. Further, the recital of prayers or a litany constitutes a kind of mental discipline which is woefully lacking in everyday existence.

A great deal of Scripture provides excellent counsel for mental hygiene. Despite the garb of archaic language, many selections from the Bible could be taken as spiritual counterparts of some of the most widely accepted psychiatric principles. In Matt. 5:28, we read: "Whosoever looketh on a woman to lust after her hath committed adultery with her already in his heart." This appears to be the earliest expression of the tenet later expounded by Freud, that the unconscious achieves socially unattainable gratification by compensatory, conscious wishful thought. Further in this same chapter it is written: "What is a man profited if he shall gain the whole world and lose his soul?" Here is a query that every coronary and ulcer victim might put to himself; in fact, every man, in our increasingly competitive civilization, could well ask himself this question. Headlong striving for material gain reaps an abundant harvest of psychosomatic disorder.

A word about Sunday schools and parochial schools is not amiss. There are many who rejoice that the uncontrollable permissiveness and undisciplined elasticity of so-called progressive education has not, as yet, pervaded the schools supervised by ecclesiastics. It must be conceded that vandalism, classroom rioting, and misbehavior in general are seldom, if ever, linked with Sunday schools and parochial schools, unless one believes that this is due to mere coincidence. Sunday school teachers provide guidance that is respected because discipline is not a sterile means of student management. Above and beyond the cultural benefits to children and adults in learning the historical background of their spiritual faiths is the fact that they are learning not by mere passive acceptance of instruction, but, as Clifton Fadiman says, by stimulation of the "desire to know."

THE PRESENT OUTLOOK

Just where do religion and psychiatry stand today? Consider the programs of the mental hospitals and state schools. At public insistence federal and state authorities have energetically sponsored chaplaincies, with ministers, rabbis, and priests as either full-time or part-time staff officers. Before they are permanently appointed they must complete a comprehensive course of psychiatric orientation. In addition to their work in institutions, all faiths participate in the support of psychotherapeutic and guidance centers. In New York City one finds the Neuropsychiatric Center of the Marble Collegiate Church, the Reis Neuropsychiatric Pavilion of St. Vincent's Hospital, and the Community Service of the Federation of Jewish Charities. Contrary to popular opinion, and to the everlasting credit of the clergymen responsible, no subject and no school of thought is taboo in any such religious psychiatric installation. While actual psychoanalytic *therapy* is not practiced at a Roman Catholic clinic, there is no prohibition of Freudian dynamic *interpretation* of mental and emotional disorders. Today's clergy are neither embarrassed by nor do they sidestep sexual problems. Rev. Revel L. Howe, director of the Institute of Advanced Pastoral Studies at Bloomfield Hills, Michigan, says, "Human love, including the sexual expression of it, needs the enabling power of divine love. This is the love that has the power to save, that is able to love the unlovable; the love that can complete our limited finite love and liberate our self-saturated love."

Severe critics of religion have frequently failed to distinguish between the finite and the infinite. It would be impossible to argue against the fact that in its finite form religion suffers from a somewhat tarnished history. In this regard, the fault has not been with religion itself, but with men who, in their eagerness to perpetuate the *institution* of their particular beliefs and to use it for selfish ends, have turned their energies to suppression, persecution, the propagation of prejudice, the encouragement of fear as the cornerstone of religion, and even war under the banners of their faiths. It is a sad paradox that the streets have run with blood, either to preserve the dominance of an institution of men or to force a new set of beliefs on a populace—in other words, murder in the name of God. The annals of man are replete with incidents of intolerance, and the blot has not yet been erased.

Yet, the scales are tipped in favor of progress. Perhaps the situation is best expressed in the words of Rabbi Joshua Loth Liebman, who speaks for both psychiatry and religion in *How Can I Believe in God Now?:*

"I have come to feel that the whole human story, with all its tragedy and its triumph, is like a page torn from the middle of a book, without beginning or end—an undecipherable page, when cut out of its context. . . . The context of man is the Power greater than man. The human adventure is part of a universal sonnet—one line in a deathless poem."

ABREACTION. A reaction to the psychoanalytic procedure in which the patient revives the memory of a repressed disagreeable experience and, by giving expression to it in speech and action, is relieved of the emotional burden that was associated with it.

ABULIA. Inability to exercise volition; indecision, a symptom sometimes observed in schizophrenia. *Cf.* Folie de doute.

ACETYLCHOLINE. A combination of choline and acetic acid, which lowers blood pressure and increases peristalsis; released by the nerves to activate muscles, it may produce hardening of the arteries.

ACROPHOBIA. *See* Bathophobia.

ADRENALIN. A trade name for epinephrine.

AFFECT. In its special psychiatric sense, this term is synonymous with emotion.

AGITATED DEPRESSION. The extreme degree of a depressed state, characterized by marked worry, restlessness, weeping, and wringing of the hands, usually accompanied by ideas of unworthiness and self-deprecation.

AGNOSIA. Loss of the ability to recognize objects or persons by perception of parts of form.

AGORAPHOBIA. A pathologic fear of open spaces.

AGRAPHIA. Inability to communicate in writing.

ALEXIA. A type of word "blindness"; inability to read although there is no organic visual pathology.

ALKALOID. Any of several bitter organic substances derived from various plants and often medically beneficial (e.g., atropine); also the vital substance of habit-forming drugs such as caffeine, cocaine, morphine, and nicotine.

AMAUROSIS. Partial or total blindness, often without demonstrable organic cause.

AMAUROTIC FAMILY IDIOCY. A familial, congenital disorder characterized by blindness, paralysis, idiocy, and a cherry-red spot on the *macula lutea* of the retina; also called *Tay-Sachs disease.*

AMBIVALENCY. Coexistence in the individual of diametrically opposed emotions, drives, or feelings, directed toward an object, or person; examples are love and hate, happiness and unhappiness, pleasure and displeasure.

AMNESIA. Loss of memory; it is *anterograde* if the "lost" memories were of events occurring after the precipitating incident (e.g., brain concussion), *retrograde,* if the patient cannot recall incidents or other data that occurred before the trauma.

AMPHETAMINE. A sympathomimetic amine, not unlike epinephrine in action, with the additional property of being able to stimulate the cerebral cortex and thus increase alertness, decrease fatigue, and encourage euphoria.

ANAL EROTICISM. Libidinal pleasure associated with bowel function, prominent in the first year of life and often reflected in later years in certain personality traits, such as overscrupulosity and miserliness.

ANALGESIA. Loss of sensibility to pain.

ANALYSAND. A person undergoing psychoanalysis.

ANALYSIS. *See* Psychoanalysis.

ANALYST. A psychoanalyst; one who is trained to administer psychoanalytic therapy.

ANENCEPHALY. Congenital absence of the brain.

ANOREXIA NERVOSA. A condition characterized by loss of appetite or inability to relish food.

ANOSMIA. Partial or total loss of the sense of smell.

ANTABUSE. A synthetic medication intended to break the habitual use of alcohol.

ANTEROGRADE AMNESIA. *See* Amnesia.

ANTISOCIAL. Exhibiting attitudes and overt behavior contrary to accepted customs, standards, and moral principles of society. *Cf.* Asocial.

ANTITHETIC TRAITS. Contradictory combinations of stated principle and real action, often observed in epileptics; the epileptic may not "practice what he preaches."

ANXIETY. A term used to describe both a normal emotional reaction to a problem or situation and a psychic affliction; in the latter, the source of apprehension cannot be identified by the subject and the anxiety is the outward expression of an inner fear.

APHASIA. Partial or total loss of the ability to communicate ideas, feelings, and desires. *Motor aphasia:* the inability to read aloud or to express oneself verbally, although the subject has formed the words and ideas in his mind. *Sensory aphasis:* the inability to comprehend spoken or written words.

APHONIA. Disturbance or loss of the capacity for producing meaningful, appropriate sounds.

APPERCEPTION. The process by which the mind is able to appreciate, evaluate, and digest an experience.

APRAXIA. The inability to manipulate objects or to put them to use in an appropriate manner.

APROSEXIA. "Absent-mindedness"; in its severest form, aprosexia prevents the sufferer from fixing his attention on a task, situation, or trend of thought, even when his personal safety is involved.

ARACHNOID. One of the membranes surrounding the brain and the spinal cord; it lies between the pia mater and the dura mater; also called *pia-arachnoid.*

ARTERIOSCLEROSIS. Hardening of the arteries, a deteriorative condition commonly manifested in persons of advanced age, but in widely different degrees. *Cerebral arteriosclerosis:* the deterioration of the vessels of the brain resulting in confusion, paranomia, or some other form of aphasia, exaggerated emotional responses, depression, and paranoid tendencies.

ASOCIAL. Exhibiting a lack of interest in or concern about the standards of one's society. *Cf.* Antisocial.

ASTEREOGNOSIS. Disturbance or loss of the ability to recognize the form of an object by touching or manipulating it.

ASTHENIC. A constitutional body type characterized by preponderance of perpendicular development over girth, with pale complexion, bluishness of ear lobes and finger tips, visceroptosis ("dropped" abdominal organs), and slow cardiac and respiratory action; believed to be associated with a withdrawn, antagonistic, often bitter personality.

ATARACTIC. Any natural or synthetic chemical agent that quiets a disturbed mental patient and relieves his anxiety and depression; also called *tranquilizer.*

ATAXIA. Inco-ordination of movement.

Aura. A subjective sensation, recognized by experience, that warns the epileptic patient of the onset of a grand mal seizure.

Autistic thinking. Thinking that is mainly subjective and detached, and that aims at gratifying desires without regard for the limitations of reality.

Autoerotism. Sexual self-attraction typical of the earliest stage of psychosexual development, the sucking and biting periods.

Automatism. Activity pursued without conscious awareness.

Autonomic nervous system. That part of the nervous system not subject to voluntary control and chiefly concerned with fundamental life processes such as cardiac action, respiration, and digestive and metabolic activities.

Babinski's sign. Extension of the large toe and spreading of the other toes when the under surface of the foot is stroked; a sign of pathology in the nervous system.

Bathophobia. A morbid aversion to depths, commonly experienced as a fear of falling from a high place and often accompanied by the impulse to jump; it is pathologic when the individual takes extreme measures to avoid being on the roof of a tall building, at the edge of a cliff, etc.

Batophobia. A morbid fear of passing between tall buildings or other high structures, or through natural formations, such as a chasm or a narrow valley.

Benzedrine. A trade name for amphetamine.

Bestiality. Sexual congress between a human being and an animal.

Binet-Simon test. A standard series of tests designed to estimate mental capacity; once the only test in general use, it has undergone several revisions and is now often supplemented or replaced by other tests. *See* Terman revision *and* Wechsler-Bellevue scale.

Blocking. Interruption of a thought trend owing to the recollection of a painful experience or emotional conflict; observed in an interview with a patient by a sudden halt in verbal response and what seems to be a refusal or an inability to proceed.

Bufotenin. An herb and hallucinogen resembling amphetamine in action, used in certain primitive rituals as a stimulant.

Buggery. A colloquial synonym for pederasty.

CA. Chronological age; one of the factors used in determining an individual's intelligence quotient.

CASTRATION COMPLEX. Fantasied loss of the penis; this reaction is usually provoked by unconscious guilt over forbidden sexual desires.

CATALEPSY. A psychogenic attack resulting in a loss of voluntary motion accompanied by stupor. *See also* Flexibilitas cerea.

CATALYTIC. Tending to alter the speed of a psychological reaction.

CATAPLEXY. Temporary loss of muscular control, with or without loss of consciousness.

CATATONIA. A type of schizophrenic reaction which may be manifested as either a stuporous or an excited state.

CATHEXIS. The direction of an emotional attachment toward a person, an object, or an idea.

CENTRAL NERVOUS SYSTEM. The entire nerve apparatus: the cranial and peripheral nerves, the brain, the spinal cord, and ganglia.

CEREBRUM. The main portion of the brain, occupying the upper area of the skull.

CHARACTER. The sum of individual traits reflecting the standards of and determined by the mores of society. *Cf.* Personality.

CHARACTER DISORDER. An emotional reaction resulting in socially unacceptable behavior, formerly categorized under *psychopathic personality;* also called *character neurosis.*

CHLORPROMAZINE. A tranquilizer (ataractic).

CHOLESTEROL. A fatty substance found in all animal fats and oils, in bile, blood, brain tissue, liver, kidneys, and certain sheaths of nerve fibers; thought to be directly related to arteriosclerosis.

CHOREA. A designation for any one of several neurological afflictions characterized by involuntary, jerky movements. *Sydenham's chorea* ("Saint Vitus' dance"): a condition seen principally in children, marked by spasmodic twitching accompanied by emotional changes and, not infrequently, by mental retardation. *Huntington's chorea:* an hereditary disease, seen in adults, the symptoms of which are irregular, uncontrollable, and, eventually, disabling movements, speech disturbances, and mental deterioration.

CHORIONIC GONADOTROPHIC HORMONE. A genital hormone found in the urine of pregnant women, which has a stimulating effect on tissue growth.

CIRRHOSIS. A condition characterized by hardening and degeneration of the liver, with yellow atrophy, due to invasion or poison (often from excessive use of alcohol); it is commonly associated with alcoholic deterioration.

CLAUSTROPHOBIA. A morbid fear of confinement or of entering small spaces.

CLIMACTERIC. A period of change, commonly used in reference to the middle years of life, when physiologic alterations, chiefly hormonal, occur in men and women; a transitional period, like that between adulthood and old age.

CLONUS. Muscular spasm of an extremity, occurring in intermittent contractions similar to oscillations.

COCAINE. A crystalline alkaloid derived from coca leaves; it is used medicinally as a local anesthetic and pupillary dilating agent, but is often employed illicitly as a narcotic.

COMPENSATION. An attempt by an individual, consciously or unconsciously conceived, to make up for his real or fancied defects.

COMPLEX. A compound of repressed emotional experiences that may significantly influence attitudes and associations. *See* Castration complex, Inferiority complex, Oedipus complex.

COMPROMISE. An emotional attitude, created consciously or unconsciously, in an attempt to resolve the incompatibility between primitive desires and the restrictions of reality.

COMPULSION. Neurotic, repetitive, stereotyped, and irrepressible activity which is the motor expression of obsessive thinking. *Cf.* Obsession.

CONDENSATION. The unconscious compression of several experiences, locations, or individuals into one idea; a mental mechanism characteristic of the dream state.

CONFABULATION. A symptom encountered in several mental disorders in which the sufferer, in response to suggestion, relates imaginary experiences, often weaving together in great detail irrelevant and unconnected ideas and events; it is frequently the result of a patient's attempt to fill the gaps caused by memory losses, but is also a normal reaction commonly encountered in children.

CONFLICT. An unconscious emotional struggle between the demands of the id and those of the ego, or between demands of the ego and the requirements of reality.

CONSCIENCE. A nonpsychiatric term for the controlling element of the mind, equated with the superego.

CONSCIOUS. Pertaining to that level of mental activity in direct contact with reality; possessing awareness and perception.

CONSTITUTION. The physiopsychologic endowment of the organism; the pattern of one's potential.

CONVERSION. A mental mechanism through which a painful emotional conflict finds outlet via bodily expression, often in a somatic symptom (rash, motor disturbance, gastric ulcer, etc.) .

COPROLALIA. Uncontrolled utterance of obscene words or phrases; commonly encountered in patients suffering from schizophrenia and the obsessive-compulsive reaction.

COPROPHILIA. A morbid attraction to human excreta, characteristic of the regressive tendency to revert to what was a normal reaction in infancy.

CORTEX. The outer layer of the brain, made up of gray cells.

COUNTERTRANSFERENCE. A reaction on the part of the analyst whereby he transfers his own emotional conflicts and repressed ideas to the patient. *Cf.* Transference.

CRANIOSACRAL. Pertaining to the parasympathetic nervous system, that part of the central nervous system that ranges from the skull to the lowest portion of the spinal cord.

CRETINISM. A condition caused by juvenile thyroid deficiency resulting in extreme mental retardation (I.Q. that of an idiot or imbecile), puffy lips and face, protruding abdomen, brittle nails, and sparse, stringy hair; a cretin's personality is "flat" and he responds poorly to training.

CUNNILINGUS. Lingual stimulation of the female genitalia.

CYCLOTHYMIA. A cycle of emotional variation in moods, of a milder form than the manic-depressive reaction.

DEFENSE MECHANISM. Any of several unconsciously provoked mental devices used to achieve a compromise between instinctual demands and the restrictions of reality. *See* Compensation, Displacement, Projection, Sublimation.

DÉJÀ VU PHENOMENON. A commonly occurring disturbance of orientation, in which the subject has the false impression that he has previously encountered the same circumstances and surroundings that he experiences at a given moment in the present. *Cf.* Paramnesia.

DELINQUENT. Descriptive of behavior that fails to comply with social (statutory) dictates; the term almost always refers to the behavior of minors.

DELIRIUM. An acute mental disturbance characterized by confusion, excitement, and disorientation, and not infrequently, by hallucinations and abject fear; it may be organogenic (due to fevers or poisons, especially alcohol) or functional in origin. *Delirium tremens:* an acute type of alcoholism, usually with accompanying physical signs such as profuse perspiration, rapid pulse, cardiac weakening, and prostration; the condition is potentially fatal unless prompt and vigorous treatment is instituted.

DELUSION. A belief arising without external stimulus and contrary to fact, as a delusion of grandeur, of persecution, etc.; it is psychogenic in origin.

DEMENTIA. Organically caused intellectual deterioration. *Dementia praecox:* an older discarded term for schizophrenia.

DEPERSONALIZATION. Loss of the sense of personal identity, usually accompanied by feelings of unreality about the environment or oneself.

DESENSITIZATION. The therapeutic process whereby the patient is required to face past traumatic and unpleasant experiences honestly.

DIPSOMANIA. A periodic, irrestible desire for alcohol.

DISCHARGE CATHARSIS. *See* Ventilation.

DISORIENTATION. Loss of the ability to place oneself in relation to time, place, or person.

DISPLACEMENT. An unconscious mental mechanism by which emotion is transferred from an unacceptable object or thought to one that is acceptable.

DISSOCIATION. An unconscious mechanism by which an idea or a group of ideas split off from the main body of the personality and become inaccessible to the conscious. *Cf.* Depersonalization.

DISTORTION. An unconscious mechanism of the dream process in which persons, places, and events that are emotionally distasteful to the dreamer, or unacceptable to the superego, are disguised or modified; the resulting substitutions are often grotesque or unidentifiable.

DISTRIBUTIVE ANALYSIS. A question-and-answer procedure in psychotherapy, in which the psychiatrist attempts to uncover all of the patient's conscious and unconscious problems, and to trace their causes through his life history, by employing many techniques, such as hypnosis, free association, abreaction, and interpretation; synthesis and distributive analysis are two aspects of Adolph Meyer's "psychobiological therapy."

DROMOMANIA. Wanderlust; an abnormal desire to travel.

D.T.'s. *See* Delirium tremens.

DUCTLESS GLANDS. The endocrine glands, whose secretions (hormones) do not require ducts in order to enter the body's vital streams; these include the pituitary, thyroid, pancreas, gonads, suprarenals, parathyroid, and thymus glands.

DURA MATER. The tough, fibrous outermost of the three membranes enclosing the brain and the spinal cord.

DYSPAREUNIA. Painful sexual intercourse.

ECHOLALIA. Irresistible repetition of a word or phrase heard; common in schizophrenia.

ECHOPRAXIA. Imitation of movement; common in schizophrenia.

E.C.T. Electronconvulsive therapy. *See* Electric shock therapy.

EEG. *See* Electroencephalogram.

EGO. That part of the basic personality structure which, through contact with the environment, becomes imbued with consciousness and assumes the role of reality-testing; the concept of self.

EGO IDEAL. An image incorporated into the ego, constructed in the early years from the attributes of significant persons in the environment, such as relatives, teachers, friends, clergymen, etc.

EGOCENTRIC. Self-centered to an extreme degree. *See also* Narcissistic.

ELECTRA COMPLEX. The female counterpart of the Oedipus complex; it involves the abnormal attachments of a girl to her father, with an unconscious sexual involvement.

ELECTRIC SHOCK THERAPY. A therapeutic procedure in which unconsciousness and convulsions are induced by passing an electric current into the brain in order to achieve modification of the patient's behavior and emotional response; also called electroconvulsive therapy.

ELECTROENCEPHALOGRAM. A recording of the electric potential of the brain; its principal use is in the diagnosis of epilepsy.

EMOTION. Affect; simultaneous physical and psychical reactions to events or situations, with both superficial and deep phenomena being elicited (e.g., raising the arms in an expression of horror and at the same time experiencing a "warm" feeling in the abdomen).

EMPATHY. A form of role-playing; identification of the self with another person, but not to the extent of incorporating the other person's attributes into the personality. *Cf.* Identification.

ENCEPHALITIS. Inflammation of the white matter of the brain. *Encephalitis lethargica:* chronic encephalitis with lethargy the prominent symptom (also called "sleeping sickness"). *Encephalitis diffusa:* a destructive and progressively degenerating brain disease characterized by visual failure, mental deterioration, and spastic paralysis (also called *Schilder's disease*). *See also* Parkinsonism.

ENCEPHALOMALACIA. "Softening" of the brain; a category which includes many injuries that result in deformities and mental deficiency at birth.

ENDOCRINE GLANDS. *See* Ductless glands.

ENDOGENOUS. Originating within the individual. *Cf.* Exogenous.

ENURESIS. Involuntary urination during sleep, most commonly functional in origin. *Nocturia;* nycturia: nocturnal enuresis.

EPILEPSY. A disorder of consciousness and motor control, with or without convulsions. *Akinetic epilepsy:* sudden postural loss, in which the sufferer may fall to the floor but will rise at once; sometimes limited to a mere nodding of the head. *Jacksonian epilepsy:* a form in which the convulsive movements are restricted to one side of the body, with consciousness usually retained. *Myoclonic epilepsy:* a condition characterized by intermittent contractions of muscles without loss of consciousness. *See also* Grand mal *and* Petit mal.

EPILEPTOID. Similar to or associated with epilepsy.

EPINEPHRINE. An active hormonal principle of the suprarenal glands; prepared synthetically it is known as *Adrenalin.*

EROGENOUS. Said of certain areas of the body (e.g., lips, breasts, clitoris, perineum) which, when stimulated, provoke sexual desire.

ERYTHROPHOBIA. A pathologic fear of blushing or of displaying embarrassment.

E.S.T. *See* Electric shock therapy.

ETIOLOGY. The total knowledge regarding the background of a disorder, embracing the life history and physiologic development of the individual, and including the possible causes of the disease.

EUPHORIA. A feeling of well-being or of capability that is either contrary or out of proportion to reality; commonly observed in general paresis and in multiple sclerosis, in which the patient, although ravaged by a disease process, insists that he is in perfect health.

EXHIBITIONISM. A morbid desire to reveal parts of the body that are customarily concealed; by extension of meaning, to "show off," to pontificate, to be the "life of the party."

EXOGENOUS. Originating from without the individual. *Cf.* Endogenous.

EXOPHTHALMOS. Protrusion of the eyeballs, a common symptom in hyperthyroidism.

EXTRAVERSION. The outward direction of psychosexual energy, revealed in such traits as gregariousness, volubility, and proneness to hyperactive motor response.

FANTASY. Reverie; a thought arising from imagination; absorption with unreality.

FEEBLE-MINDEDNESS. *See* Mental retardation.

FELLATIO. Lingual excitation of the male genital organ.

FETISH. An inanimate object, capable of arousing sexual feelings, that is used as a symbolic substitute for a person.

FIXATION. Arrest of the libido at any of the stages of psychosexual development prior to heterosexuality, leading to inappropriate or abnormal personality characteristics.

FLAGELLATION. Whipping, or having oneself whipped, to obtain sexual gratification.

FLEXIBILITAS CEREA. A waxlike flexibility of the extremities, in which a limb remains in whatever position it is placed; a common sign in catatonia.

FLIGHT OF IDEAS. An abnormally rapid outpouring of associations, in which the patient frequently shifts the topic, does not return to his original point, and never reaches the goal of his narrative; in a milder, usually nonpathologic form, this is called *circumstantiality.*

FOLIE DE DOUTE. A mental state in which the subject is assailed by abnormal scruples and anxiety over even the most elementary, everyday tasks and activities; hair-splitting distinctions are made on minor points, and conclusions are continually revised and restated.

FREE ASSOCIATION. Spontaneous and uninhibited verbal response by a patient undergoing psychoanalysis; a technique employed to uncover the background of an emotional conflict and other unconscious material.

FREE-FLOATING ANXIETY. Scattered and unattached anxiety which the patient cannot explain to his own satisfaction.

FRUSTRATION. The thwarting of a drive for gratification, either by the external demands of reality or by dictates of the conscience, or superego.

FUGUE. An unconsciously motivated flight from reality in which the subject performs apparently purposeful acts but seems to be in a dream state.

FUNCTIONAL. Involving the physiologic action of an organ or a complete organism, but not affecting its structure; commonly used, though not quite accurately, as a synonym for Psychogenic.

GERIATRICS. The branch of medicine dealing with the health problems of the aged.

GERONTOLOGY. The scientific body of knowledge embracing all aspects of the process of aging.

GLUTAMIC ACID. A pharmaceutical preparation reported to have produced improvement in the total personality functioning of mentally retarded persons, with a subsequent slight increase in the intelligence quotient.

GONAD. A sex gland; either an ovary or a testicle.

GRAND MAL. The severe form of epilepsy; the attack is usually preceded by an aura or warning, and has the form of violent muscular activity—convulsion, collapse, loss of consciousness, usually with tongue-biting and sometimes evacuation of the bowel and bladder; when consciousness is regained headache, nausea, depression, and amnesia for the seizure may ensue.

GRAPHORRHEA. Uncontrolled, purposeless writing of long lists or letters, words, or symbols; seen occasionally in schizophrenia.

GRIM HUMOR. A reaction encountered in delirium tremens, in which the patient laughs at visual hallucinations that are actually frightening him.

HALLUCINATION. An impression not based on true sensory perception; it may involve distortions of any or all of the five senses; a common symptom in several forms of mental disorder.

HALLUCINOSIS. A state characterized by recurring hallucinations. *Acute hallucinosis:* a transient reaction, seen commonly in acute alcoholism, in which the hallucinations are accompanied by abject fear.

HEBEPHRENIA. Pathologic lassitude and indifference; a progressively deteriorating form of schizophrenia characterized by inappropriate affect, childishness, introversion, and usually, by hallucinations and delusions.

HEMIPLEGIA. A paralytic stroke involving one side of the body.

HEROIN. A habit-forming narcotic derived from morphine.

HETEROEROTISM. Direction of sexual feeling toward persons of the opposite sex or toward objects other than the self.

HETEROSEXUAL. Pertaining to libidinal attachment to the opposite sex; descriptive of the mature state in psychosexual development.

HOLISTIC APPROACH. A diagnostic-therapeutic viewpoint in which the psychiatrist, regarding the patient as an entity, takes into account his physical constitution, injuries and illnesses, environment, heredity, and the cultural pattern in which he moves. *Cf.* Psychobiology.

HOMATROPINE. A drug used to dilate the pupils, a diagnostic adjunct.

HOMOEROTISM. Love for the same sex. Also called homosexuality. *Cf.* Heteroerotism.

HOMOSEXUAL. Pertaining to libidinal attachment to the same sex; descriptive of a stage in psychosexual development that follows narcissism and precedes heterosexuality. *Latent homosexuality:* the homosexual drive, conscious or unconscious, that is not granted overt expression.

HORMONE. Any one of several endocrine gland secretions, which functions chiefly as a stimulant and is capable of producing an effect on cells other than those where it originates. *See also* Epinephrine, Gonad, Insulin, Thyroid.

HUNTINGTON'S CHOREA. *See under* Chorea.

HYDROCEPHALUS. A cogenital anomaly characterized by dilation of the ventricles of the brain, with marked enlargement of the skull (the result of overproduction of cerebrospinal fluid); commonly described as "water on the brain."

HYPALGESIA. Decrease in sensibility to pain.

HYPERGLYCEMIA. Abnormal increase in blood sugar.

HYPERINSULINISM. A syndrome characterized by loss of consciousness, with or without convulsions, resulting from oversecretion of insulin by the pancreas; as a method of treating mental disorders, it may be induced chemotherapeutically.

HYPERKINESTHESIA. Exaggerated sensitivity to kinesthetic stimulation. *See* Kinesthesia.

HYPERPROSEXIA. A form of obsessive-compulsive reaction in which the subject is absorbed by one idea to the exclusion of all others.

HYPNOSIS. A sleeping state, induced by suggestion, in which the subject carries out directions or, under urging, reveals suppressed or repressed information; useful as a psychotherapeutic technique.

HYPOCHONDRIASIS. Unreasonable concern over one's health, usually in the absence of any organic pathology; a psychoneurotic reaction.

HYPOMANIA. A milder form of the manic phase of manic-depressive psychosis; restlessness, distractibility, and flight of ideas are observed, but frenzied overactivity and destructiveness are absent.

HYSTERIA. A psychoneurotic disorder arising from an emotional conflict, in which repressed material finds an outlet through sensorimotor disturbances, such as blindness, loss of certain sensations, and paralysis of the limbs, with loss or impairment of speech function. *See also* Conversion.

ID. That portion of the psyche which is the repository of instinctual drives.

IDENTIFICATION. Conscious or unconscious role-playing wherein the individual assumes the attributes and behavior of another person or persons; at the conscious level, employed in moderation to enhance self-esteem, it is a beneficial merchanism; under unconscious control it may prevent the subject from establishing the integrity of his ego.

IDIOCY. The severest grade of mental retardation (mental age under three years) ; the idiot is incapable of attending to the most elementary personal needs and of protecting himself against even the most ordinary dangers; idiocy is commonly accompanied by serious handicaps in the sensorimotor fields and physical anomalies. IDIOT SAVANT: an idiot endowed with some unusual talent in a restricted area of mental activity (such as the ability to recall a long series of license numbers observed at a given time), but in whom other intellectual activity is minimal.

IDIOPATHIC. Having no known or discernible cause, although the symptoms may be easily observed.

ILLUSION. A falsely interpreted sensory perception, such as the optical illusion of an oasis in the desert, or the auditory illusion of a wind heard as wailing or singing.

IMBECILE. A mentally retarded person whose mental age is between three and seven years (i.e., a child with an intelligence quotient between 24 and 49) ; the imbecile is less incapacitated than the idiot but is only slightly trainable and unable to support himself independently in the community.

INCOHERENT. Descriptive of speech made up of jumbled words or unrelated, scattered ideas; common in manic-depressive psychosis.

INFERIORITY COMPLEX. The constellation of ideas and emotions surrounding feelings of inadequacy, usually given expression in tyrannical or boastful behavior or some other reaction in a mood of assumed superiority.

INK-BLOT TEST. *See* Rorschach test.

INSULIN. The hormonal secretion of the pancreas. *See also* Hyperinsulinism.

INSULIN SHOCK THERAPY. A method for the treatment of the major psychoses whereby coma is induced in the patient to interrupt his psychotic trend. *Cf.* Hyperinsulinism.

INTELLIGENCE. The innate ability to cope with new and unexpected changes in the environment; the capacity for perception and understanding.

INTELLIGENCE QUOTIENT (I.Q.). A value derived from tests and mathematical computation which indicates the level of intellectual capacity in an individual. *See also:* Binet-Simon Test *and* Wechsler-Bellevue Scale.

INTROJECTION. The unconscious process of assuming the feelings of another person, usually accompanied by a reaction to those feelings as if they were one's own.

INTROVERSION. Inward direction of the libido, reflected in the tendency to shun interpersonal relations and to be absorbed by egocentric ideas. *Cf.* Extraversion.

INVOLUNTARY. Functioning independently of conscious control.

INVOLUTIONAL PSYCHOSES. A group of several types of pathologic reactions occurring from middle life to the onset of old age; the principal characteristics are depressive or paranoid trends, uncontrollable fits of crying, and feelings of unworthiness or failure.

I.Q. *See* Intelligence quotient.

KAINOPHOBIA. Morbid fear of new things, persons, or situations.

KATATONIA. *See* Catatonia.

KLEPTOMANIA. A compulsive drive to steal, in which there is little or no concern over economic gain from the stolen goods.

KINESTHESIA. The sensation of movement, action, or balance, derived from the nervous elements associated with the muscles and controlled by the vestibular apparatus in the inner ear.

KORSAKOFF'S REACTION. A form of chronic alcoholism marked by disorientation, confabulation, retention defects, and frequently, by peripheral neuritis.

LATENT CONTENT. The part of the dream which, owing to the censorship of the superego, is disguised by symbols but which may be uncovered through psychoanalysis, thus revealing the persons, situations, or ideas which are distasteful to the dreamer. *Cf.* Manifest content.

LESBIAN. An overtly homosexual female.

LIBIDO. Energy or force, most commonly used to describe two vital human instincts, sex and the will to live.

LOBECTOMY. Surgical removal of a small segment of the frontal lobe of the brain to effect a salutary change in the personality of the subject.

LOBOTOMY. Surgical entry into the frontal lobe and severing of certain neural connections within the brain to promote improvement in the condition of a mentally ill person.

LOGORRHEA. Uncontrolled and continuous speech, usually repetitious, but coherent.

MA. *See* Mental age.

MAGIC OMNIPOTENCE. An unconscious feeling of supreme power over one's environment; refers especially to the attitude of infants but is also encountered in schizophrenia.

MANIC-DEPRESSIVE PSYCHOSIS. An affective psychosis in which the symptoms are predominantly expressed in emotional outbursts or apathy, hyperactivity or hypoactivity, elation or depression, often with mood swings between the extremes of these characteristics.

MANIFEST CONTENT. The aspect of the dream that can be recalled by the subject; the dream as the dreamer relates it after waking, but which, unconsciously, he tends to embellish with modifications acceptable to his ego or to the demands of society.

MARIJUANA. A narcotic derived from *Cannabis indica,* which is not habit-forming but may pave the way for drug addiction; employed to promote orgiastic behavior or libertine sprees, it induces macroptic and microptic hallucinations and disturbances of the senses of time, space, and position; under its influence the subject often feels an unwarranted and unrealistic sense of skill.

MASCULINE PROTEST. An emotional reaction rooted in the cultural pattern, believed by Alfred Adler to be fundamental in personality development; generated by the concept of masculine "superiority" in the male, it is expressed as anxiety over living up to the masculine role; in the female it is a protest against the fact that she is not a man.

MELANCHOLIA. Profound sadness; morbid grief, or grief that outlives a reasonable duration.

MENOPAUSE. Cessation of menstruation, usually between the ages of forty-five and fifty; may be the precipitating factor in mental illness for some maladjusted individuals. *See* Involutional psychoses.

MENTAL AGE. The numerical equivalent of an individual's intelligence in relation to others; one of the elements used in determining the intelligence quotient.

MENTAL DEFICIENCY. *See* Mental retardation.

MENTAL RETARDATION. The more accepted term for mental deficiency or feeble-mindedness; this term embraces the holistic concept of medicine, recognizing the emotional development and total personality traits of an individual in addition to his intelligence level.

MESCALINE. An hallucinogenic drug derived from the weed mescal, originally used by primitive peoples as an excitant during tribal rituals.

METABOLISM. The sum of all the physiologic processes by which food substances are broken down and assimilated and wastes are separated and eliminated; by this process, energy is made available to the organism. *Basal metabolism:* the minimum expenditure of energy required to sustain life in the organism.

MICROCEPHALY. A congenital anomaly in which the head is abnormally small.

MONGOLISM. A form of congenital idiocy, so called because the facial features resemble those of a Mongol (flattened skull and slanted eyes); despite their retarded intellect, Mongolian idiots are often lively and imitative and are amenable to some training.

MONGOLOID. Having characteristics similar to but not so severe as those of Mongolian idiocy.

MORON. A mentally retarded person whose mental age is between eight and eleven years (or a child with an intelligence quotient between 50 and 69); morons are capable of limited training for performing simple tasks and can be self-supporting in the community under close supervision and guidance.

MORPHINE. An alkaloid of opium, a powerful analgesic and narcotic drug.

MOTOR APHASIA. *See under* Aphasia.

MUTISM. A state of speechlessness due to a brain lesion, malfunction of the vocal apparatus, or negativism in mental patients.

MYOCLONUS. Intermittent hyperflexion or twitching of a muscle or group of muscles.

NARCISSISM. Self-love; the stage of psychosexual development following the autoerotic stage, from which it differs in that the development of the ego has begun.

NARCOANALYSIS. A psychotherapeutic procedure used for uncovering and probing into underlying emotional problems and breaking them down into their basic components; it is carried out with subject in a drug-induced sleeplike state.

NARCOLEPSY. A disorder of consciousness marked by a sudden overwhelming desire to sleep no matter where the subject is or what he is doing.

NARCOSYNTHESIS. A procedure similar to narcoanalysis in which the patient relives his emotional reactions to past traumatic experiences in an attempt to re-evaluate and understand them.

NIHILISTIC DELUSION. A delusion, encountered in schizophrenia, that the environment, or large elements of it, have vanished, often expressed in the following ideas: "There are no more people," "The earth has disintegrated," "Life has ceased."

NYCTOPHOBIA. Fear of the darkness or of the approach of night.

NYMPHOMANIA. An abnormal, persistent desire in the female for sexual intercourse. *Cf.* Satyriasis.

OBSESSION. A constant, irresistible preoccupation with a single thought or complex of thoughts, observed commonly in neurotics. *Cf.* Compulsion.

OEDIPUS COMPLEX. An abnormal, prolonged attachment of a male for his mother, frequently with incestuous overtones; so called after the central character in the classical (Sophocles) story of Oedipus' love for his mother.

OMNIPOTENCE.. *See* Magic omnipotence.

ONTOGENETIC. Arising during or pertaining to the life of the individual. *Cf.* Phylogenetic.

OPIUM. The alkaloid juice of the poppy, analgesic in action; a powerful narcotic drug.

OPPENHEIM'S REFLEX. Extension of the great toe when the middle portion of the inner border of the tibia is stroked; it has the same significance as *Babinski's sign.*

ORAL STAGE. The earliest phase of the autoerotic stage of psychosexual development in which persons, situations, and surroundings are perceived and interpreted exclusively in the light of their relation to the feeding process.

ORGANIC. Arising from the living organism; pertaining to an organ or organs.

ORGASM. The climax of sexual excitation; it is accompanied in the male by a discharge of semen, and in both sexes by the swelling of erectile tissue and a sense of pleasure and relaxation.

ORIENTATION. The process of placing oneself in relation to time, place, and person; usually lacking or faulty in psychotics.

ORTHOPSYCHIATRY. A branch of psychiatry specializing in the understanding and treatment of mental and emotional disorders of younger persons, in which the stress is on prevention and mental hygiene.

OXYCEPHALY. A congenital anomaly in which the skull has an unusually high vertical index; colloquially referred to as a "pinhead."

PAIN. In its special sense in psychiatry, pain refers to disagreeable, embarrassing, or guilty feelings, often unconsciously experienced and therefore not recognized by the subject at the level of awareness; also called "psychic pain."

PARALYSIS AGITANS. *See* Parkinsonism.

PARAMNESIA. Confusion over the details of past experiences, often exhibited as the inability to separate reality from fantasy. *See also* Déjà vu phenomenon.

PARANOIA. A major psychotic reaction characterized by suspiciousness and egocentricity woven into the pattern of a highly organized, often complex system of persecutory delusions; there is often a strong homosexual component.

PARANOID. Pertaining to, originating in, or similar to paranoia; applicable to any unorganized persecutory trend of ideas seen in senile psychosis, schizophrenia, or other mental disorders, where the specific structure of true paranoia is not present.

PARASYMPATHETIC NERVOUS SYSTEM. The craniosacral division of the autonomic nervous system; its principal constituent is the vagus nerve, which is involved in the nervous control of the viscera.

PARATHYROIDS. Four buttonlike ductless glands located in back of the thyroid gland; hypofunction of the parathyroids leads to tetany.

PARESIS, GENERAL. A form of brain and spinal cord syphilis characterized by widespread neurological changes and mental deterioration; in its most advanced stage locomotion is impaired, speech becomes slurred, and there is loss of judgment, profound memory defect, and a decreasing regard for propriety; euphoria and delusions of grandeur are common.

PARESTHESIA. Any false or distorted sensation, usually of touch or of body surfaces. *See also* Phantom limb.

PARKINSONISM. A neurological disorder due to pathology involving one part of the brain's motor system; a form of encephalitis; its common symptoms are muscular rigidity with irregular movements, festination, scanning speech, masklike facial expression, and drooling.

PAROSMIA. Disturbance of the sense of smell.

PEDERASTY. Sexual intercourse per anum, usually of an older man with a boy; another, somewhat synonymous term, *pederosis,* implies sexual relations with immature girls.

PELLAGRA. A deficiency disease caused by a lack of vitamin B_2; in addition to the characteristic skin lesions and gastrointestinal disorders, mental symptoms such as confusion, memory impairment, and hallucinations are frequently encountered.

PENIS ENVY. An early aspect of psychosexual development in the female, when knowledge that the male possesses a penis may stimulate unconscious feelings of inferiority and a longing for a similar organ.

PERCEPTION. The mental mechanism by which objects are recognized and their functions understood.

PERIPHERAL NEURITIS. Inflammation of nerves surrounding the brain and spinal cord.

PERSEVERATION. Pointless, unchecked, compulsive repetition of words or phrases; the pace of the verbalization is not necessarily as swift as in logorrhea.

PERSONALITY. The total picture of behavioral characteristics by which one is recognized as an individual. *Cf.* Character.

PETIT MAL. A mild form of epileptic seizure, in which consciousness is only briefly lost (from a few seconds to a minute) ; the sufferer may experience slight confusion or none at all; several such attacks may occur in one day.

PHALLIC SYMBOL. Any object resembling the penis, such as a tower, church spire, obelisk, pencil, post, etc.; it is often used as a symbol in a dream or in the thought processes of psychotic or psychoneurotic persons.

PHALLUS. The penis.

PHANTOM LIMB. A sensation of some amputees, in which the subject ascribes feelings to an amputated limb.

PHENYLPYRUVIC OLOGOPHRENIA. A form of mental retardation caused by the presence of phenylpyruvic acid in the body system, believed to be due to prenatal influences or birth trauma.

PHOBIA. A morbid, abnormal fear, usually without adequate cause.

PHOTOPHOBIA. Pathologic fear of light; abnormal sensitivity to light.

PHYLOGENETIC. Originating or related to the successive stages in the evolution of the species. *Cf.* Ontogenetic.

PHYSIOLOGIC. Pertaining to the physical functions of the living organism and its component parts.

PIA MATER. The innermost of the three membranes that enclose the brain and the spinal cord; it contains a network of blood vessels. *See also* Dura mater *and* Arachnoid.

PINEAL BODY. A glandlike organ situated in the brain; it produces no internal secretion and its function is unknown.

PITUITARY GLAND. A ductless gland situated in the brain, regarded as the "regulator" of the endocrine system.

PLEASURE PRINCIPLE. The guiding motivation in infancy, later modified to conform to the restrictions of social living.

PORENCEPHALY. A congenitally deficient, cystic condition, characterized by cavities in the brain matter.

PRECONSCIOUS. The level of mental activity from which data, concepts, and experiences can be recalled readily; such material is seldom associated with emotional conflict or the deeper drives; it is the level of ordinary, everyday memory association; also called *foreconscious*.

PREFONTAL LOBOTOMY. *See* Lobotomy.

PRESBYOPHRENIA. A form of senile psychosis in which, while there is general mental alertness, memory defects are encountered for which the sufferer compensates by confabulations.

PRIAPISM. Pathologic, long-maintained penile erection without ejaculation.

PROJECTION. An unconscious mental mechanism by which an inner perception, upon reaching the conscious level, is treated by the individual as if it applied to or emanated from an external source.

PSYCHE. The mental dynamics and thought content of the individual; the mind.

PSYCHIATRIST. A doctor of medicine who, after pursuing prescribed studies, has been certified as a specialist in the diagnosis and treatment of mental disorders.

PSYCHIATRY. The science of the study, diagnosis, and treatment of mental disorders.

PSYCHOANALYSIS. In its specific sense, a therapeutic technique, originated by Sigmund Freud and modified by Horney, Fromm, Reik, etc., in which pathologic reactions are investigated by psychologic procedures such as free association and dream analysis; in its general sense, an approach to the understanding of the dynamics of personality oriented towards Freudian concepts.

PSYCHOBIOLOGY. An approach to mental illness, introduced by Adolph Meyer, in which he urged that diagnosis and treatment be based on the interaction of the patient's inherited structure, tendencies, and life experiences with the stresses of his environment. *Cf*. Holistic approach.

PSYCHOMOTOR EQUIVALENT. An epileptoid condition characterized by momentary impairment of consciousness, with purposeful movements and, in some instances, violent displays of emotion.

PSYCHONEUROSIS. An emotional illness which reflects an unconscious attempt to resolve a maladaptation due to conflict between the id and the ego; while in some of its forms it is incapacitating, a psychoneurosis, unlike a psychosis, does not destroy the integrity of the personality, and contact with the environment is preserved.

PSYCHOPATH. A former term used to describe a *sociopath,* i.e., person suffering from a character disorder.

PSYCHOPATHOLOGY. The science dealing with the nonorganic aspects of mental disorder.

PSYCHOSEXUAL. Pertaining to the mental aspects of sexuality. *Psychosexual development:* the mental and emotional development of the individual from birth to maturity, culminating in satisfactory heterosexual adjustment.

PSYCHOSIS. A major mental disorder principally characterized by deviant, often bizarre, behavior and withdrawal from the normal stream of life; some of the symptoms commonly present are regression, hallucinations, delusions, disorientation, and verbalization of aberrant ideas.

PSYCHOSOMATIC. Descriptive of bodily symptoms which are expressions of inner emotional conflicts.

PSYCHOSURGERY. Any of several brain operations undertaken to relieve or check a severe mental disorder. *See also* Lobectomy, Lobotomy, and Topectomy.

PSYCHOTHERAPY. The treatment of mental and emotional disorders by nonphysical methods.

PYKNIC. A type of physical constitution characterized by large body cavities, rotundity, short neck, and heavy shoulders; generally typical of persons who are given to wide mood swings.

PYKNOLEPSY. A variety of a petit mal attack, in which the loss of consciousness is so brief in duration as to be scarcely noticed by other persons present.

PYROMANIA. A morbid, irresistible drive to commit arson for erotic satisfaction.

RATIONALIZATION. A mental mechanism by which the subject provides a socially acceptable explanation for a thought, feeling, or action which, if permitted outward expression, would induce in him a sense of shame or embarrassment.

RAUWOLFIA SERPENTINA. An herb used as a tranquilizer and sedative.

REALITY PRINCIPLE. The acquired motivation for socialized behavior resulting from the need to modify the wholly egocentric drives of infancy. *Cf.* Pleasure principle.

RE-EDUCATION. Specifically, that phase of the psychoanalytic technique that follows the uncovering of unconscious motivation, in which the patient, possessing insight into the background of his personality disturbance, is presented with a program for handling conflictual situations as they may arise in the future.

REGRESSION. Reversal of psychosexual development; a form of schizophrenic reaction, with the sufferer resuming the postures and behavior of infancy.

REPRESSION. An unconscious mental mechanism whereby distasteful thoughts and drives are excluded from the conscious level and thus the true nature of a painful emotion is not recognized.

RESERPINE. A tranquilizing agent.

RETROGRADE AMNESIA. *See under* Amnesia.

RORSCHACH TEST. A diagnostic device in which the patient's reactions and verbal responses to prescribed ink-blot forms are used to uncover and interpret emotional and ideational trends significant in certain mental disorders.

SADISM. A drive to obtain satisfaction, usually of a sexual nature, by inflicting pain on other persons, or on animals.

SAINT VITUS' DANCE. *See under* Chorea.

SAPPHIST. *See* Lesbian.

SATYRIASIS. Excessive sexual desire and activity in a male. *Cf.* Nymphomania.

SCANNING SPEECH. Deliberate, staccato speech, with discernible pauses between syllables, produced with apparent difficulty; encountered in Parkinsonism.

SCHILDER'S DISEASE. *See under* Encephalitis.

SCHIZOID. Like or pertaining to schizophrenia.

SCHIZOPHRENIA. A major psychosis, characterized by introversion, regression, childishness, asocial (possibly antisocial) behavior, hallucinations, delusions, depersonalization, and aberrant ideas.

SCHNAUZKRAMPF. Uncontrolled pouting, a symptom occasionally observed in schizophrenia.

SCOPOPHOBIA. Pathologic fear of being seen; a scopophobiac will insist that window shades be drawn, or may keep his eyes tightly closed; it is a common sign in schizophrenia.

SENSORIUM. The combined perceptive capabilities of an individual, including the special sense organs and their centers in the brain.

SENSORY APHASIA. *See under* Aphasia.

SOCIOPATHY. A personality disorder primarily expressed through inability or unwillingness to conform to prevailing mores and dictates.

SOMA. The body.

SPASM. A sudden involuntary muscular contraction.

SPASTIC. Pertaining to a rigid condition of a muscle or group of muscles; relating to or the result of a spasm.

SPINA BIFIDA. Congenital failure of the spinal column to close, thereby rendering it susceptible to herniation.

STANFORD SCALE. *See* Terman revision.

STATUS EPILEPTICUS. An advanced degree of grand mal, in which convulsion follows convulsion with little or no intermission.

STEREOGNOSTIC PERCEPTION. Identification of familiar objects solely through the sense of touch.

STEREOTYPY. Repetitive thinking, speaking, or acting in an unvaried pattern; a common symptom of schizophrenia.

STREPHOSYMBOLIA. An emotional state in which, although vision is intact, the subject fails to learn by ordinary teaching methods; it often takes the form of reversal of letter and word order.

STUPOR. A mental state characterized by a decrease in, or absence of, responsiveness, giving the impression that the subject "refuses" to react to sensory stimulation; commonly seen in catatonia, hysteria, and narcolepsy.

SUBLIMATION. An unconscious mental mechanism whereby consciously unacceptable instinctual demands are channeled into acceptable forms for gratification, e.g., aggressiveness converted into athletic activity, the mother instinct into teaching, etc.

SUBSTITUTION. An unconscious mental mechanism by which an unattainable or unacceptable object, goal, or feeling is replaced by one that is socially acceptable.

SUBTHALAMUS. That part of the brain believed to be concerned with emotional control.

SUGGESTIBILITY. The tendency to respond almost automatically; the suggestion may be verbal, or it may arise from some situation, event, or physical feature of the environment.

SUPEREGO. Freud's term for that part of the personality developed early in life, primarily from parental influence, which is roughly synonymous with conscience.

SUPPRESSION. Conscious muffling of painful feelings or ideas. *Cf.* Repression.

SUPRARENAL GLANDS. The ductless glands situated on the poles of the kidneys, which secrete epinephrine, a stimulant of the central nervous system; also called the *adrenals.*

SURROGATE. A substitute, e.g., an employer, teacher, or nurse who takes the role of a parent.

SYDENHAM'S CHOREA. *See under* Chorea.

SYMBOLISM. An unconscious mechanism employed in dreaming by which the subject disguises persons, objects, and situations that have painful emotional associations for him.

SYMPATHETIC NERVOUS SYSTEM. The division of the autonomic nervous system which is responsible for innervating the smooth muscles and the ductless glands; it is concerned with such involuntary actions as dilation of blood vessels and release of glandular secretions.

SYMPATHETONIA. Predominance of the sympathetic over the parasympathetic nervous system, resulting in such physical symptoms as flushing, dilation of the pupils, increased heart action, etc.

SYMPATHOMIMETIC. Acting in the manner of the sympathetic nervous system; said of the effects of various drugs.

SYNCOPE. The fainting or swooning state; a disturbance of consciousness resulting from an interruption in the supply of blood to the cerebrum.

TABES DORSALIS. A symptom of general paresis, with the patient exhibiting unsteadiness of gait, attacks of excruciating pain, pupillary changes, and loss of certain reflexes.

TAY-SACHS DISEASE. *See* Amaurotic family idiocy.

TENSION. In the psychiatric sense, emotional "tightness"; edginess accompanied by anxiety.

TERMAN REVISION. The American version of the Binet-Simon intelligence test as evolved by Dr. Lewis M. Terman of Stanford University; also called the *Stanford revision.*

TETANY. A manifestation of parathyroid insufficiency, characterized by spasms of the hands and feet.

THRESHOLD OF CONSCIOUSNESS. The point at which a stimulus is perceived; this threshold is lowered in stuporous states.

THYROID. A ductless gland situated in the neck, whose secretion (thyroxin) is intimately associated with the body's metabolic activity.

TOPECTOMY. Surgical removal of a portion of the cerebral cortex in order to modify the behavior and bizarre mental processes of the psychotic.

TRANQUILIZER. Any natural or synthetic chemical agent that quiets a disturbed mental patient and relieves his anxiety and depression; also called *ataractic.*

TRANSFERENCE. An unconscious shift of libidinal attachment; a stage in the psychoanalytic technique wherein the patient transfers his antagonism from the disturbing "characters" in his underlying emotional conflict to the psychiatrist. *Cf.* Countertransference *and* Abreaction.

TRANSVESTISM. A sexual perversion in which the subject has the impulse to dress in the manner of the opposite sex.

TRAUMA. In the psychiatric sense, emotional shock causing psychic pain.

TRUTH SERUM. A popular term for sodium amytal or pentothal sodium, barbiturates used in narcosynthesis and narcoanalysis.

TUBEROUS SCLEROSIS. A disorder of unknown etiology characterized by the appearance of small nodules under the skin and accompanied by convulsive seizures and mental retardation.

UNCONSCIOUS. That portion of the mind, or psyche, that is rarely subject to awareness and is the repository for repressed data and instinctual drives. *Personal unconscious:* according to Jung, the complex of repressed ontogenetic experiences, in contrast to the *collective unconscious,* that part which embraces the phylogenetic (racial) heritage.

VAGOTONIA. Predominance of the vagus nerve and/or the parasympathetic nervous system. *Cf.* Sympathetonia.

VEGETATIVE NERVOUS SYSTEM. *See* Autonomic nervous system.

VENTILATION. The expression of formerly repressed material by the patient as he relates his emotional difficulties.

VERBIGERATION. Repetitive, incoherent, usually uncontrolled loquacity.

VISCERA. The internal (principally, the abdominal) organs.

VOLITION. Conscious initiation of action; a synonym for "will."

VOLUNTARY MUSCLE. A muscle that is contractible at will.

VOYEURISM. A form of sexual perversion in which erotic satisfaction is gained by viewing a sexual symbol or sexual activity; a voyeur is commonly known as a *Peeping Tom*.

WECHSLER-BELLEVUE SCALE. Commonly used intelligence tests, differing only slightly from the Terman revision of the Binet-Simon test; Wechsler takes into account the percentage distribution of each of the intelligence levels.

WORD BLINDNESS (DEAFNESS). Inability to understand the written or spoken word although the visual and auditory senses are intact; it is due to an organic lesion in the brain. *Cf.* Alexia.

WORD SALAD. A form of speech common in schizophrenics, with words and phrases that have no apparent significance or logical coherence for the hearers.

XENOPHOBIA. Uneasiness or fear in the presence of strangers or in strange surroundings.

Index

Index